A **Commitment**
to *Compassion*

Reflections from a Life of Service

Dear Sharon
Hope you enjoy this
book as much
as I did
Jing

A **Commitment** to *Compassion*

Reflections from a Life of Service

AVRAM R. KRAFT, MD, FACS

In collaboration with
Rachel E. Kraft and Susan J. White

AMARNA
BOOKS & MEDIA
www.amarnabooksandmedia.com

ISBN-10: 0-9828951-9-4
ISBN-13: 978-0-9828951-9-1

www.acommitmenttocompassion.com

Published by Amarna Books & Media, Maplewood, New Jersey

www.amarnabooksandmedia.com

Table of Contents

READER NOTES

- Terms and scripture defined and explained in the Glossary are *italicized* in the text.

- Writing "G-d" in place of "God" is a Jewish custom to avoid the risk of writing the name of G-d and eventually risk erasing or defacing the name.

- In the following interview format, Avram R. Kraft is referred to as **ARK** and Rachel E. Kraft is referred to as **REK**

Dedication

My profound gratitude
to my beloved spouse and best friend,
Kerana Gladstone Kraft.
I dedicate this book to her.

Our mutual call to service brought us together.

Because she understands me so well,
she has been able to not only fiercely support me,
but also challenge me and love me so beautifully
these past six decades.

There has been no better advocate.

Heartfelt gratitude to my family and friends for
their loving kindness, support and candor.

I am humbled by their openness and boundless energy,
enthusiastic encouragement and presence.

Each has contributed to the
beauty and meaning of my life.

....

"Marching to a different drummer is not a failing,
but more developing a keen sense of hearing."

—*Avram R. Kraft, MD*

....

Foreword

"Your father would stay up all night and hold someone's hand if he thought it would make a difference."

During my formative years, my mother would say this with what felt like equal parts frustration and pride.

This was also her answer when I asked, "Why do people say that Dad isn't your typical surgeon?"

"Your father would stay up all night and hold someone's hand if he thought it would make a difference."

At that age, I did not yet appreciate that surgery was a specialty that attracted a personality often described as arrogant, impersonal and egocentric. An all-around poor communicator.

And yet, my father is none of those things. Even at the age of 7 or 8, I could appreciate that an arrogant, impersonal, egocentric surgeon with poor communication skills would probably not stay up all night and hold someone's hand in the hope that it would make a difference.

In the world according to Avram R. Kraft, MD, listening, embracing and caring contributed to a medical practice that enabled healing not just of the body, but of the heart and soul.

A Commitment to Compassion grew out of many conversations with Avram, patients, fellow caregivers, family and friends. It explores the *art* of bringing compassion to medical care and real compassion to any of our interactions.

It's been a privilege to discuss this period of his life, hear the stories of his earlier years—which would shape the man and doctor he would become—and discuss with him those issues with which he continues to wrestle.

That perhaps has been the most profound. I idolized this man as a child, admired him as a teenager, was in conflict with him as a young adult and finally, as a more mature individual, could recognize our similarities and differences and see that he is very human, like the rest of us. And perhaps most poignantly for me, I now recognize that no matter how accomplished, he is *still* filled with self-doubt and questions like all of us.

"Your father would stay up all night and hold someone's hand if he thought it would make a difference."

As I begin my own personal intermission after three decades working in theater, I am grateful to remain so close to this kind of personal storytelling that provides as much insight into my own stories, strengths and frailties as it does to those of my father as storyteller.

Most of all, it reminds me that seeing another person, giving them your time, gives them the space to tell *their* story. Little did my father know when he began his particular path as a doctor that part of his healing practice would include bearing witness to his patients' lives, and thus their stories, providing them a compassion, and dare I say love, that they were not expecting when they picked up the phone to make an appointment.

Rachel E. Kraft, December 19, 2017

. . .

ADDENDUM

I sent this Foreword to my father on the day I wrote it, waiting for an acknowledgment of the draft and assurances he was comfortable with the message. I didn't hear back because the next day he suffered his second stroke in six months. The "Acceptance of Self" chapter was an interview that began two months after that stroke.

Rachel E. Kraft, April 22, 2018

....

"Story can often be the difference between sanity and despair. We need story and beauty, and wit and imagination, like we need food and air."

—*Martha Lavey,*
Steppenwolf Theatre Ensemble Member
and Past Artistic Director

....

Preface

Who am I?

What am I?

What am I all about?

What am I trying to say?

Why is it important?

Does it have application beyond me?

How do I thank the people who made my life possible— made me who I am?

These are the questions for which I have been searching for answers since I was a young boy. They are no different from your questions, I suspect.

And if we look at death not as the cessation of life but as a transition of our spirit to another place, then thinking about mortality and attempting to understand the meaning of the life here and now and the existence of a hereafter prompts me to both look back and search forward.

I would like to think that we all try, in our own way, to contribute to what's going on in the world—to make it a better place. This is an existential question that challenges this writer in this complicated world of ours.

In the grand scheme of things, we live profound yet microscopic lives. How do I take responsibility for who I am in the world in a way that has meaning beyond myself, that hopefully speaks to other people—especially young people—who are choosing a path of intentional giving, to other fellow human beings?

Why make the effort? Why spend time looking back over a life of lessons learned? Why try to put them together in a cohesive format that may be meaningful to others? It is because of the generosity of spirit of the ones who did this for me, and my obligation to build on that and share it.

Often, the best most of us have to offer this world is our caring. Love is not something that should be contained. Love is big and open-ended and like the proverbial pebble dropped in the water, sending larger and larger ripples out across the surface, generating a much greater effect than what we see at its focal beginning.

If I do anything in this world that has meaning, it will be to share the awareness of the love I have within myself: to love family, community, humanity and the Divine. This love is boundless and can be present in the endless and unexplained encounters this life presents.

Service given from a place of love has the best chance of being received positively by the recipient.

And where does love typically begin—but in the home. And where do we first find exposure to service—but from those we look up to.

An early lesson at the foot of my father, Harry Kraft, *of blessed memory (a Jewish expression to honor the deceased)* set my thinking in place on this subject. At the time, my younger brother and I were both pre-*Bar Mitzvah* age. As happens with kids, we were provoking each other as two siblings in a shared space will do.

But on this day, we really went at it and were tangled such that the commotion brought our dear father between us. He was visibly agitated and turned to me, the oldest, saying, "What's the matter with you?! You are his senior; you should be setting an example!"

Without batting an eyelash, I retorted, "Why should I? *AM I MY BROTHER'S KEEPER?*" In an instant, our gentle, otherwise loving parent backhanded me across the *punim (Yiddish for face)*. He was trembling when he said, "NEVER, EVER LET ME HEAR YOU SAY THOSE WORDS AGAIN. Yes, you *are* your brother's keeper and never, ever, forget it."

I had never felt the sting of my dad's hand before and never did again. At the time, I felt shame—but as with all pivotal moments in one's development, it was also a critical opportunity for self-examination and growth. What was my father really saying to me?

Dating back to the biblical source of the brothers Cain and Abel, we have a responsibility to one another. Without wearing that mantle, what are we?

A life of service requires a focused approach. Our world is bigger than us, and we are responsible for those around us who make up the fabric of our lives. And when there are unexpected, rapid and sharp life turns, we must honor that it's the universe pointing out a time to review and reassess where we've been and where we're going.

I propel myself by the dictum of *naaseh v'nshmah (Hebrew for "act and hear").* The whole quote is "act and hear, do the *mitzvah*—the good deed—and then reflect, learn and teach." Engagement is not just doing and learning, but also sharing and encouraging the next person to be as involved as you are. In this way, you extend yourself into the world.

And as if that isn't enough, what is our responsibility to self along the way? For without love of self, and looking for the joy in the day, what do we have to share with our companions on this journey?

I am speaking to you as a person, not a doctor, not someone with all of the answers, or even *any* of the answers.

I am just a fellow seeker of answers, wanting to share my questions and life experience, and I invite you on the journey.

Won't you join me?

Avram R. Kraft, MD

....

"The most beautiful people we have known are those who have known defeat, known suffering, known struggle, known loss, and have found their way out of those depths."

—Elisabeth Kübler-Ross, Swiss-American psychiatrist and a pioneer known for her theory of the five stages of grief

....

"My earliest memories of Avram were of him in action at Beth El in Highland Park where he emerged as a steady, elegant voice when the synagogue was between professional cantors. I vividly remember as a child coming to Shabbat services and hearing Avram celebrating Jewish life in prayer. To this day, his voice sings with a smile, and I'm told it has distinct traces of his father's chanting. I began admiring him when I was young and in my own way was in awe of him.

I ended up serving in the synagogue where Avram grew up, and it was incredibly moving when I reconnected with him as an adult. His sense of compassion for people is at the core of who he is, and he is a deeply spiritual person. There's no question that he recognizes that we can each liberate the potential for G-d's work in these miraculous bodies that we are given as a gift. He understands that there's a whole level of meaning that is not corporal or visible, but quite real.

I am delighted that he has chosen to share his views in these interviews with Rachel."

—*Rabbi William Hamilton,*
Congregation Kehillath Israel,
Brookline, Massachusetts

Compassion
in Action

REK: Compassion. That is our starting point.

ARK: I see our time together as an exchange of ideas, of life stories and personal philosophy highlighting the theme of compassion in life experiences. Over a lifetime, we identify ourselves more completely with the human condition and come to recognize and understand the intimacy of learning the depth of compassion of one person for another. A sensitive human being develops a sense of what it's like to be a human being. Because of your own human needs, you recognize what pain and suffering are. This makes you a more complete person. The more experiences you have, the more complete you are as an individual, and the more capable of identifying with the joy and suffering of your neighbor.

REK: If sympathy is feeling compassion and empathy is putting yourself in someone else's shoes, what do you strive for?

ARK: For me, sympathy is a primal response to someone else's suffering—a generic approach to an individual life. For me, it's not an adequate enough response to the human condition because I believe that each of us has a higher degree of responsibility to one another.

Empathy, then, represents the leveraging of our energies in the recognition of the next person's humanity. It makes us more aware of whom they've become because of a willingness to hear, listen and identify in order to understand someone else's needs. You are actually putting yourself in a secondary position to better understand someone else's needs instead of putting your own stamp on someone based on what you *think* they need.

REK: It means getting involved. It can mean things could get messy.

ARK: If we're going to identify with someone else's pain and suffering, then we take on not only a willingness to listen, but also a strong identity with that person's life circumstances. This sense of bonding compels us to assume responsibility for something to alter it. And that's where sympathy, empathy and compassion intersect—not just recognizing someone else's pain, not just identifying with someone's discomfort, but also knowing that these feelings must be coupled with an urgency to be involved.

This has been my calling. To bear witness, to listen and— to the best of my ability—to put myself in service to another. Sometimes it included harnessing my skills as a doctor, but just as often it meant being present. Really being with someone. Giving them the space to trust and share. And with them, building a plan for care. ✍

....

"Too often we underestimate the power of a touch, a smile, a kind word, a listening ear, an honest compliment, or the smallest act of caring, all of which have the potential to turn a life around."

—*Leo Buscaglia, an American author and motivational speaker, also known as "Dr. Love"*

....

Choosing a Life of Service

REK: My memory is always of you "being of service." As a doctor and friend. Even if your service was "just" being present.

ARK: It's been the greatest honor of my life to find ways to serve my fellow man. In some ways, I think this path chose *me*.

REK: In terms of…

ARK: I had my own brushes with health issues from birth. I had a *brit milah (Hebrew referring to a Jewish male circumcision ceremony on the eighth day of the infant's life)* and developed a post-op infection for which I was hospitalized. It was 1938, the year the first systemic antibiotics were introduced, and my mum thought I was a goner.

During WWII, I underwent a tonsillectomy at home under open drop ether. I was 5 and experienced a post-op bleed.

Maybe that accounts for why when I was a youngster, I never sought care for a fractured middle finger playing softball or the repair of a soft tissue leg gouge injury from a hockey laceration. Probably it had more to do with the reality that both those injuries occurred on *Shabbat (Hebrew for Sabbath)* when I wouldn't have brought it to my parents' attention because it would have been inconsistent with "the day of rest" and what it represented to any observant Jew.

I did finally need to seek treatment to remove a steel fragment from my eye at the age of 12, in 1950. I would work for my father every summer. I was a packer and a shipper for my dad at The Crown Dress Manufacturing

Company near Chinatown in Boston. I had to use a strapping machine to bind cases of house dresses, and it had an automatic cutting device. One day, something fractured off and a fragment of steel struck the sclera of my left eye. I was sent to Joe Skirball, our pediatrician. In turn, he sent me to his brother Louie Skirball, an ophthalmologist down the hall. So, under topical anesthesia (all that was offered at the time), and with a certain confidence that was bred from the person he was, Louie operated on my eye and removed a steel fragment.

Years later, with a sense of pride, I was invited to interview as a medical student at the Skirballs' alma mater, the University of Vermont. Upon arriving on campus, I remember scouring the walls until I found the brothers in a photograph near Hall A, at the site where I would hear, on admission, lectures in basic medical science.

Looking back, it's powerful to me to realize that my pediatrician, an alum of the University of Vermont's Medical School, referred me to his brother, also an alum, who performed a delicate surgery on yours truly, who would one day be a student of that same medical school.

Who could have known that day that this surgery would protect my eyesight—so I could go on to be a surgeon myself. In retrospect, I was overwhelmed with an earth-shattering awareness. My eyesight was preserved as if it was *b'shert (Yiddish for destiny)*, for a purpose.

Fortunately, there was little personal operative excitement over the following decades until I failed a stress test in my 50s and had a five-vessel coronary bypass graft.

REK: You believe the early brushes with your own health steered you toward medicine?

ARK: Perhaps. I was encouraged by my parents to be a *rabbi* or a physician. In those days, those were the choices for their oldest, and I took my parents' recommendations very seriously.

Luckily, a family friend named Moshe Lieberman said early and often, "He's not cut out for the politics of the *rabbinate*." And so, I became a doctor.

REK: Did it seem like a natural fit?

ARK: I believe it was. With every interaction, we have the opportunity to begin by improving ourselves, to anticipate someone else's need, to effect change and potentially to inspire someone to do the same. And in the process, to bring the world closer to G-d's intent to make this the best place for humanity to thrive. In this way, we glorify the Divine. And this I believe, this is our purpose, in this world, to leave our mark through our actions. Serving as a physician was my vehicle for this work.

Early on, I would trust an intuition about what the people around me needed. It could be a small thing like making the bed and shining the shoes of my younger brother with whom I shared a room, knowing that otherwise our mum would come down hard on both of us.

As the oldest sibling, I had an awareness that my parents expected more of me—and that began with working hard and excelling at school to set the proper example for my brother and sister.

When I was in my teens, I remember vividly a teacher of mine at the Hebrew College in Brookline, Egon Lewin. This man's entire family had been wiped out in the Holocaust. I could see and feel the huge burden he carried of this early devastation. I saw him as a man in great pain, and my devotion in his class became my naïve way of trying to ease it.

REK: Why him?

ARK: Intuitively, I felt a closeness to him—the power of his having experienced such immense pain and how it must have impacted him in his quiet, unassuming way. I did not know him well but felt I was drawn to him by all he had been through. It made me conscious of the importance of reaching out to someone suffering, in pain, and in need of healing.

In some very deep place, I can see that his world—having witnessed all that he had—had an impact on me. I saw what and how prayer meant to him and how he tried to make the presence of being in a state of prayer—of praising the Divine—a key component of his life beyond words. That he still chose to serve and was a humble servant of the Divine awakened in me a deep sense of belonging to the Jewish spiritual world.

REK: Early inspiration.

ARK: Service lifted me out of my mediocrity in a certain way. Instead of just existing, I wanted to have a chance to speak to a higher purpose in my life.

I have experienced almost a magnetic pull in my personal and professional life to ease pain. We can each do that in different ways. Medicine was the means by which I achieved that goal.

My own definition of compassion means being in a state of relating to another person's suffering and hoping to be able to do something to relieve that suffering. I think my intense desire to help relieve suffering is one of the reasons I went into surgery.

REK: I know Grammy, your mom, had a hard start in life, something you were very aware of.

ARK: My mum, Sarah Webber Kraft, experienced an early trauma in her life which I can't begin to pretend to understand. She was living in Canada and was a victim of the Halifax Explosion of 1917 (a maritime disaster in Nova Scotia, Canada, in which a Norwegian vessel collided with a French cargo ship carrying explosives—making it the largest man-made explosion at the time—and caused a tsunami-like tidal wave of destruction).

She sustained temporary blindness and multiple facial lacerations. This event occurred while her parents were in Montreal arranging an older sister's marriage. A local veterinarian undertook her care at the time. Hearing family stories like that kindled an early desire to alleviate human suffering by assuming responsibility to treat.

REK: Another eye trauma.

ARK: Indeed. My father, Harry Kraft, similarly sought to play a giving role, and I studied his behavior from an early age. He was a lay leader in my childhood synagogue, assisting the professional staff and leading the children's services. I still hear from my peers and from his grandchildren that to be in his presence and to experience his joy of life and Judaism was contagious. Each of us can play our own role. Some pursue service professionally, but it is not the only path.

REK: As a friend of mine is fond of saying, every light side has a dark component. Is there a parallel in the world of service?

ARK: A fair question and a good question, albeit a hard one. But service can be married to hardship and comes at great risk. My own father, whom I watched so carefully, wanted to ease the pain and bring his community closer together. Trying to do so much for so many comes at a cost, and without conscious awareness I have found myself repeating that pattern in my own life.

When you have a calling to do service of this kind, one should constantly be re-examining motives, priorities and limitations. This includes gifting yourself enormous compassion and discipline in order to make an impact and avoid the tendency to overextend and "burn out." I have found that by focusing on both self-compassion and self-discipline, I can better accept when to call a personal "time out" to tend to my own very legitimate needs. This remains something with which I continue to wrestle to this day, and it is a worthy struggle. ✍

....

"If I could give you information of my life, it would
be to show how a woman of very ordinary ability has
been led by God in strange and unaccustomed paths
to do in His service what He had done in her. And if
I could tell you all, you would see how God has done
all, and I nothing."

—Florence Nightingale, English social reformer
and founder of modern nursing

....

Dignity

REK: What attracted you to medicine?

ARK: It was the honor that my mother placed on the art of caring for the suffering. And the touch point was her witnessing her father's premature demise when she was around 11 years old. And she, in turn, had also witnessed a commitment her father had placed on relieving chronic respiratory ailment. The family had a history of this illness, and my maternal grandfather eventually died of end-stage asthma.

REK: What was your grandfather's field?

ARK: His field was ingenuity with a commitment to healing. This was the man I was named for. He was an inventive person who found niches based on whatever his exposure was to a set of given circumstances. He was a pragmatist who owned a fox farm on Prince Edward Island to pay the bills. His inventive spirit also led to developing what he named as an "anthasthma" device to relieve the wheezing distress for persons hungry for air. He himself could relate as he suffered from respiratory limitations imposed on his frail frame. You must imagine what that was like—someone desperate for the calming effect of oxygen as it bathes his nostrils.

REK: It must have been hard on your mom to see him in distress.

ARK: Witnessing this living distress on the part of a loving parent energized her and led to her wanting to encourage her first born, named after her father, to enter the healing profession.

REK: And with these expectations you enter the medical field.

ARK: For me, it went from the more global perspective of medicine to the more particular focus of the suffering individual—what we now call patient care, about giving dignity back to a patient.

When we are vulnerable, we are at our most exposed and needy. You see that so often with someone grappling with a condition of a medical unknown. A want on the part of the individual is to receive reassurance that there is an intervention that has elements of healing associated with it. And sometimes there's just not one specialist who can bring clarity and resolve the given issue. The boundless search for ultimate resolution becomes an intense hunt on the part of the patient and a committed family.

In the process, the patient and the family can be left exhausted and demoralized. I believed that as a caregiver I could be a presence to guide the search and hopefully this would stabilize the concern of the individual and/or family, improve their outlook and strengthen a commitment to shoulder the ongoing search to find answers.

REK: So, guiding the search for answers was part of your caregiver's responsibility. I have also heard you talk about the need for a caregiver to focus on dignity for your patients. How was that cultivated in you?

ARK: I had an experience as a third-year medical student at the University of Vermont that actually shaped the way I would practice medicine over the subsequent decades. I was rounding with fellow students and a board-certified internist who was a proven excellent clinician. We walked into a patient's room and this physician turned to us, his students, and asked, "Why is this patient's skin color yellow?" He proceeded to lift the sheet and uncover the patient's privacy, revealing a frail, elderly person in a urine-stained gown who was exposed and defenseless.

I felt a physical revulsion and found myself cowering at the side of the bed, thinking immediately that the shell of humanity had been totally abandoned. In trying to test our diagnostic abilities, this doctor had made the patient a prop, disregarding that he was treating him like a specimen in an experiment whose sole purpose was to be of service to us.

This is a challenge in any teaching hospital. Students need to learn and hands-on experience is imperative, but sometimes the price may be too high. There must be a contract of trust between physician and patient. It is sacred and inherently demands respect. If the patient is going to accept the medical staff into their world, then the physical space between them demands an awareness that the patient knowingly compromises their privacy in order to train the next generation of healers.

In that moment, I told myself that I would never show that kind of disregard to a patient—that I would never treat patients with such an absence of respect. That encounter, both disappointing and illuminating, guided me; I was able to turn that negative experience into a positive inspiration for how I could practice medicine. It also brought a new urgency to the integrity I wanted to bring to my every interaction with people in and out of the medical care setting.

In practical terms, I made a commitment to myself that I wouldn't stand at a bedside, "towering" over people. I would pull up a chair or ask if I could sit on the edge of the bed. That began when I was a medical student, and it carried on through my practice.

REK: What can you learn at eye level? What can you diagnose that you might miss otherwise?

ARK: It is both your eyes being open and applying your knowledge.

As Chief Resident in Boston at what was then known as the Deaconess Hospital and is now known as Beth Israel Deaconess Medical Center, I had nursing home patients referred to my service. I made up my mind that when I cared for those patients, I would treat them in the kindest way possible. These individuals were priceless to me and from the most vulnerable of populations—survivors, of the Holocaust, immigrants from many nations, often without family members, neglected by the system. I always tried to treat all of my patients with compassion and kindness, but I felt these particular residents needed the utmost of care. They were frail survivors.

Looking at them directly, holding their hand and offering a personal greeting can make a real difference when one is feeling more or less powerless over one's life.

REK: Dignity has remained a theme throughout your life. When you chaired the Ethics Committee at Highland Park Hospital, you and your colleague Dr. Philippe Cochran, who then followed you as chair, worked hard on making the value of dignity front and center for the hospital.

ARK: Philippe and I shared a fierce desire to advocate for those without a voice. We worked together on establishing the "Inappropriate Medical Care Policy."

We had long been interested in preserving the rights of patients struggling with end-of-life care. And we had all seen instances where families were torn apart and patients suffered unduly as a consequence, but it took two particular cases to galvanize us. Both cases were brought before the Ethics Committee.

The first case was a woman in her 90s who was depressed and had been treated with supportive therapy, including medication. Her psychiatrist recommended electroconvulsive therapy (ECT, shock therapy).

Her son favored this course of treatment. Hospice recommended that her situation be reviewed by the Ethics Committee because this woman herself had asked that she be allowed to die without benefit of any further intervention.

The psychiatrist came before the Ethics Committee and spoke to how vital a person she was and her choice not to have ECT was because she was depressed. The son wanted to follow the recommendation of the psychiatrist, to potentially reverse her condition so she could continue to live as a vital 90-year-old.

The Ethics Committee felt she had already had a full, mature therapeutic intervention, from a board-certified psychiatrist, and it was their recommendation that If her choice was not to continue treatment, and to end her life naturally, then that was totally acceptable.

Despite the committee's recommendation, the patient's son insisted that the hospital provide ECT therapy. She had some improvement in her psychological depression but suffered the ill effects of ECT, including confusion. When she was discharged from the hospital, she was in a dependent state, *not* as vital as she had been.

The second case was again a 90-year-old patient. She had chronic inflammatory lung disease that caused obstructed airflow to and from the lungs. She was facing respiratory failure. She was on CPAP (continuous positive airway pressure) and still needed additional support. Continued treatment would require that she be intubated until such time as she could come off the ventilator. But under the circumstances, if she went on it, she wouldn't come off of it unless it was to die.

Bottom line, she didn't want to be hooked up. She wanted to live out her life without further medical intervention. But her energy was depleted from labored breathing, and she said her adult children would decide for her. The children were split on what to do, and the case was brought before the Ethics Committee. Most regrettably, two of the children even threatened the care team with the expectation that the staff keep their mom alive. The Ethics Committee later learned that the children went to court to resolve the matter. The sad irony is that their mother died that day they were in court.

In both cases, the patients' intentions got lost amidst well-intentioned family members whom they trusted. And so, it raises the question of whose life is it anyway? Whom do we as caregivers protect?

We studied some of the most progressive policies at the time from California and put together our own "Inappropriate Medical Care Policy." We lobbied the hospital's administration, and following exhaustive legal reviews and our impassioned efforts, the policy was adopted. I believe that policies like this one can serve as a critical force for compassion and dignity.

REK: End-of-life care and communication around this incredibly charged topic is another area where you have felt called to serve.

ARK: I think as a society we are slowly moving in the right direction, paying more attention to the idea of dying with dignity and communicating with formal advance directives about what we want our end-of-life care to look like.

Yet there's still so much reluctance to talk openly about death, both generally and specifically, to ourselves, our family and our caregivers. The fear and sense of taboo surrounding death in our culture restrict people from facing their own mortality and having tough conversations with their spouses and children about what's important to them. Yet it can be incredibly reassuring and comforting in a sense to spell out your wishes and know that you can have some control and can maintain dignity as you live your final days.

REK: And how does that play out in your personal life?

ARK: I remember writing my first living will before my first open-heart surgery when I was 56 years old. It was written the night before I had surgery. I wanted to take responsibility for having planned and thoughtfully stated all the implications of any statement I had made about receiving care. It was important to me that I had an obligation to be a partner with my caregivers in this process. I believed that it was a shared responsibility between patient/family and caregivers. I was also thinking in particular for my wife, a health provider herself. If any tough decisions needed to be made, I wanted her to know that I wanted to be privy to that information and I wanted there to be a partnership between the caregiver and the care recipient. There should be dignity around the vulnerability as a patient.

REK: At this point in life, do these conversations take on extra weight and meaning as you navigate your own health challenges?

ARK: Yes, I do feel closer than ever to my own mortality. Yet in the Jewish tradition and in my own faith, I believe there is a world for us after living in this temporal world. We're taught that it will be a time of blessed reunion, meeting the other souls with whom we've yearned for reconnection.

There's an old Jewish tale of the Almighty and the prophets sitting at a table with a white tablecloth, constantly singing mystical melodies, as part of an entry into *Olam HaBah (Hebrew for the afterlife).* As I love to sing and have always found great joy in the mingling of voices, I imagine these melodies as a bridge to life after death. Thinking about it this way makes it a little less threatening to me and a natural transition to living beyond this life.

REK: How so?

ARK: I had a dream recently. I was in Jerusalem, the sun was shining, the sky was a deep blue and I was amidst a group singing, and the layers of voices were rising in a beautiful way. Suddenly, I awoke and my pulse was racing. I was concerned enough that I checked it and it was 30 beats higher than customarily. In my weekly study, my teacher proposed that this was a preview of my presence in the world to come. That interpretation was calming to me, such that I could embrace it as a friend and not an ominous presence.

My health scares have made me think more about my meeting with my maker. *(At the time of this particular interview, Avram had had two TIAs and two strokes in a 14-month period.)* If there is meaning to our dreams, then mine encouraged me to inquire of myself: Was I suitably there for others given what I was capable of, and did I embrace those I encountered with sufficient openness and caring?

REK: Every day, I see you bringing a concern of dignity for the people with whom you interact. I experience that as a core value for you. Is our work ever done relative to this inquiry?

ARK: In my 8th decade, I think I have even greater perspective, because I'm willing to question myself, my motivations and my assumptions. I can listen even more attentively and hopefully be a better witness to my fellow man. At any age, we can honor the value of someone's questions, even help them frame their questions and assist them in the process of finding their answers. ✍

"The most luxurious possession, the richest treasure anybody has, is his personal dignity."

*—Jackie Robinson, first African American
to play in Major League Baseball*

Power of Touch

REK: In the mid-'70s, when we moved to our community in Highland Park, Illinois, our family often heard from people that you were not a typical surgeon. What do you think people meant by that?

ARK: A surgeon is a doctor who is trained to be expedient: to get in and get out safely. To identify a problem, incise and excise it, and move on. My attraction to medicine was the desire to make a difference—and certainly in a concrete, definitive and respectful manner—but it was more than that.

Surgeons are sometimes critiqued for working as if on an assembly line. Next! So, for patients with that perception, a doctor who was willing to sit with them and explain a disease, an intervention, possible outcomes and even complications—a doctor who asked if he could hold their hand before they were rolled into surgery, a doctor who was in their room after surgery to personally see if he could do anything—that seemed to surprise people. It was very rewarding, personally, to witness someone relax if they had entered in a state of agitation. Identifying with someone's anxiety and responding to it can go a long way for people in the most vulnerable situations. I learned these lessons in my life as a caregiver, but they're certainly applicable beyond the medical or professional realm. Letting people know that I care became a guiding force in my life.

REK: How did you come to that?

ARK: My father *of blessed memory* was exemplary. He taught me the primacy of attentiveness, respect for each person you encounter, the love of the Divine, and an awe for our presence in the world and our parallel role in the holy task of the individual to do their part in the world in meeting someone else's needs. It's a mighty obligation. I even wondered if I was doing this for my father or for myself. Was I altering myself? YES! But I believe I was not denying my own creative energy—rather, I was harnessing my attention to the lessons I learned from him.

REK: How did you come to terms with that?

ARK: It's been a lifelong journey. I felt that I was on a journey of love. That is to say, the embrace that I experienced by being hugged by my father was enveloping and was scented by his presence and created an energy force that was *his* ability to love. That was translated by me as a giving life force that I in turn wanted to, and did, share with others in need of care as I had been fortunate to receive as Harry's child.

Another lesson from my father was through *menachem avel (Hebrew for consoling mourners).* As a child, I would often ask my father where he was going, and he said *menachem avel zein (Yiddish meaning to visit and comfort mourners).* The *mitzvah (Hebrew for commandment, with a secondary meaning of good deed)* to reach out to the mourner is a longstanding Jewish tradition and an extension of the whole impetus to love. My father visited not only family and close friends, but also anyone he knew in his community who had suffered a loss. He made people feel better because it was through his love that he cared for the next person. They felt his presence in our community. People saw his healing outreach. As I reflected on the importance of this practice to him, I took away a message that I could play my part. This became an unspoken desire to heal suffering from loss.

"Ki ani Hashem rofecha" (Hebrew for "For I am the Lord that heals you," Exodus 15:26). My father's dictum to me was you have a spiritual obligation to be a healer as our Lord is a healer. Being a healer means being a spiritual connection to a grander world.

When I graduated from medical school, my father wrote a quote in a *Chumash (Hebrew for the five books of the Torah)* that he gifted me. The message I took from him was his recognition of the Healing Path, and G-d as a healer, and an acknowledgment of G-d as the spiritual guide so that I in turn could be a healer for others.

Alas, my father's life ended when I was just 40. I was a husband and the father of two children. I was working in the medical profession and reflected how my practice of caregiving was directly impacted by both my parents' influence on my life. In parallel to my father, though with different language and influence, my mother Sarah also primed the pump as she had been deeply impacted by her own father's illness and his passion to heal himself and others' suffering.

Trans-generationally, she saw the validity and value of the healing sciences in name and kind *(see also Dignity on page 35)*. Together, my parents set me off on a life mission of healing.

My father gifted me an appreciation of the love of the Divine. So when I suffered the loss of his physical presence in my life, instead of just cursing the dark and my loss, I learned to channel the gifts of my father to help others heal while healing myself through service.

REK: You see touch as part of the healing process. And I recognize that (my brother) Adam has learned the value of touch from you. From a young age, I can remember his following your lead and hugging and kissing everyone at *shul (Yiddish for synagogue).*

ARK: I remember that fondly as well. It was normative in my upbringing for men in the community, not just family, to greet with a hug and a kiss. I know there were times when both Adam and I received surprised and probably some uncomfortable responses to our demonstrative behavior, but we persevered and soon, others were following suit!

But it is more than seeing touch as part of the healing process. It is bearing witness to the human condition. And sometimes, the touch is as healing for the physician as it is for the patient or the family.

REK: I can see how that would be healing for a patient. How does it benefit the caregiver?

ARK: There's an awareness you develop that you don't have to limit your boundaries. Using your tactile senses is yet another way to gather information about what you encounter. It enhances what your eyes can see. If the physician is willing to take that risk, it means he or she is willing to connect more deeply with the patient and enter their zone. It provides the patient added value. You introduce the warmth of your compassion to a patient by holding a hand or offering a hug. You share that elementally with the other person to whom you're reaching out and are healed in turn.

REK: I'm feeling like there's a particular story that comes to mind for you.

ARK: There is. It involves the violent death of a young boy. And it is a moment from some 30 years ago that I will remember forever.

Everything about that day is etched in my memory. It was sunny. After making our morning rounds, my partner and I were breaking for coffee for our customary rambling chat ranging from religion to sports. We were interrupted by an overhead page for all surgical teams to report to the Emergency Department (ED).

We quickly learned that on this morning in 1988, a disturbed person inexplicably and randomly shot a cluster of children at a local elementary school.

Three of these youngsters were taken to our ED at Highland Park Hospital. My partner Ed Margulies and I were assigned to care for a child who was stable with an abdominal wound. In the panorama of my peripheral vision, I saw a colleague working with rapid movements on a small child while a third team was resuscitating another youngster.

I'm not quite sure what drew me away from "our patient" to the second victim. As I approached the gurney, I saw that the child's pressure monitor displayed a flat line. The surgeon already had his hand in the boy's chest, massaging his heart which he reported as being empty of fluid despite multiple intravenous lines running wide open. At that moment, nothing made a difference.

The bedside nurse said, "It's over." The physician tore off his gloves, said to her, "You close," and turned away to treat someone else, anyone else. The nurse was speaking quietly to me and said, "You know, he has a son the same age." I told her that I wanted to help; we started closing the chest wound together.

The moment seemed to last a lifetime. This child looked so peaceful. His skin was still warm. His name was unknown to me at that moment, though his name would become known to the community as the only fatality of that terrible rampage. We finished. I was about to step away from his gurney and return to the tumult of the fray around me when I saw our first patient being wheeled toward the operating room (OR). I held up my hand, five fingers extended, asking for five more minutes. My partner nodded.

The nurse and I washed and then wrapped our unknown child in a clean, white sheet. I told the nurse, "I need to hold him." The impulse to do this was spontaneous. I didn't know why. I hugged him and kissed his cooling forehead. What an inexplicable tragedy, I thought. Do his parents even know that he's here? Will they ever know we cared? I gently handed this small, now lifeless body to the nurse and went off to the OR.

REK: You needed to hold him.

ARK: Yes. I wasn't ready to let go of him. I think I wanted to send him off with the firm knowledge that he was loved. While the touch was for him, *I* also needed that hug. I needed that moment for my own composure as I reconciled that no amount of medical expertise that day was going to keep him with us. 🌊

....

"Nobody cares how much you know until they know how much you care."

—*Often attributed to Theodore Roosevelt, 26th President of the United States from 1901 to 1909*

....

Acceptance
of Self

REK: You've been on quite the journey over the past six months. Two different types of strokes. Your recovery has been remarkable, but I know there are areas in which you still struggle.

ARK: Yes, it's very humbling. I am blessed with my speech and movement. I'm frustrated with myself, though, that I can so easily become overwhelmed by what I've lost — including the ability to drive and the need for a caregiver by my side because I suffer from "left-sided neglect" (an inability to perceive space on the left side, in contradistinction to a visual field impairment).

REK: We were at Barbara and David Hoffman's home for *Shabbos (Yiddish for Sabbath)* dinner after your most recent stroke. It was time for the "blessing of the children" and as is our custom, I stood up for your fatherly blessing. You put your hands on each side of my head and I awaited the familiar message in Hebrew that begins *"Y'simeach Elohim k'Sarah, k'Rivkah, k'Rachel, uk'Leah"* (Numbers 6:24-26), meaning "May G-d make you like Sarah, Rebecca, Rachel and Leah." It became apparent after a number of seconds that you couldn't find the words to get started. David, seemingly intuitively, figured out what you needed and gave you the first word *Y'simeach (Hebrew for "May G-d make you like")*, and you were back on track.

As I told you at the time, you handled that moment with great dignity and grace. At least that's how it felt to me on the outside. What was going on for you on the *inside*?

ARK: Internally, the reaction I commonly experience in response to some threatening illness or potential loss is anxiety, then anger. Anxiety because I don't know what's in store for me. Anger because I feel out of control. In all of my current life experiences—daily, professional, personal, spiritual—I'm working with a personal philosophy of "your goal is to attain equanimity of self-expression, a place of balance, as if these challenges which may be daily can only be countered by seeking some middle ground." Searching for balance and experiencing life is the strategy to achieve this goal.

So, this is what happens when I become reactive to someone or something. My initial response is what you've typified. I get anxious, and then angry, and then have to find my way back.

REK: So, the anger is turned internally?

ARK: Yes. So, I *try* in those moments to let it come, let it hit me in the face. It's a life test, an opportunity to accept what's there, what's real, what's creating a feeling of imbalance and generating all the various mind states. Let it be. See what you face, and does it make sense in the context of the moment and how can it best be analyzed? What talents do you have to counter this imbalance? How can they be applied to move in a tangible direction, a direction towards resolution? How do you exercise your capacity to control something that felt inescapable?

REK: And in that moment at the *Shabbat* dinner table?

ARK: I knew there was a path to resolution that would be timely. I didn't know what it was, but recognized if I were patient it would present itself.

REK: Wondering, but I don't want to put words in your mouth. Dickens. Best and worst of times. Rare gifts can surface in situations we would not have chosen for ourselves.

ARK: My take is patience, unhurried and un-harried. This has allowed me to find my way, post strokes, through dark tunnels. Self-confidence that comes with patience, internal calm. Instead of anticipating, I try to let them be what they are. That's been my greatest aid in finding my way through recent difficulties.

REK: But literally, what was going on in your head when you couldn't remember the two words, if you don't mind my asking?

ARK: I accepted the fact that I'm vulnerable and that it was embarrassing. When I was searching for words, I found myself trying to process what was going on inside me. I wanted to give you a *Shabbat* blessing and needed a jump start. David intuitively understood and gave me the prompt I required. As soon as I had the first word, I was okay and could proceed.

REK: Still, that must have been difficult in a room full of people.

ARK: I have a memory of a time in the operating room and feeling that I was in over my head. I recognized it served me and the patient, and in that moment, it was better to look for help than tough it out alone. I accepted my vulnerability and asked the OR staff to find my partner. I could have felt very inadequate at that moment and maybe I did—I subsequently asked myself, who counts? Was it the patient or me? I knew I had to do everything I could to ensure that this patient could handle this assault to his body.

Bottom line, there was only one person who counted, and that was the person who couldn't speak for himself. It requires being in a state of equanimity, and that requires recognition that if I ever needed help, I would be able to ask for it.

REK: So, you had to put ego to the side to focus on your primary objective whether it was blessing your daughter or taking care of a patient. Good modeling around the fact that we don't have to pretend to be what we're not or pretend to know what we don't.

ARK: Marries into the idea that no man is an island.

REK: In medicine, I assume you saw a lot of islands.

ARK: The idea was that you need to be an independent thinker and actor and that the only way to move forward is to battle the hard stuff as independently as circumstances allowed. I found it difficult to accept that dictum. It wasn't something I chose to live by. And yet I was brought up to think it was the only way to live. To fail, struggle and find the answers on your own. Marching to a different drummer is not a failing, but more developing a keen sense of hearing.

REK: When did you realize your moving to a different drummer was not a failing?

ARK: In gradations. There were multiple opportunities for me to see that I had different strengths from people I admire and that we would and could complement each other. That certainly happened in my medical practice. And I also saw that manifest itself in our Sabbath study group, birthed after the death of my father, as my way to continue his legacy of Jewish study and discovery.

Shortly after we moved to Highland Park, Illinois, 10 couples met every other Saturday afternoon to study a portion of religious text. It became, though, a larger conversation about life and personal philosophy woven into the fabric of our debate, grounded in our faith and struggles with our faith. You could see up close how people processed information. We all brought something to the table and helped one another expand our understanding.

To have a community of people witness your life milestones has been a rare and precious gift.

Study has been a salve for me in dark times and a driving force to better understand myself and my tradition.

What happened on Friday night—when I could not remember the beginning of the blessing—is essential to understanding the basic elements that motivate me to be who I am and why. I want to be the best human being I can. I have to be human and not some idealized form and recognize where I'm frail and how I deal with my own vulnerability.

REK: But I suspect that didn't come to you overnight? What's it like for you to be a patient, especially after years of wearing a very different hat as doctor/healer.

ARK: It requires self-acceptance and patience. It's like putting the brakes on time and not being in a rush, not accelerating but guiding my thoughts to be paced. An essential part of my learning and finding answers is that I need to put the brakes on when I become anxious or rushed because anxiety never contributes to finding answers. Another component is my father. I imagine my father's capacity to be loving, caring, patient and determined to do the right thing.

REK: You're carrying him with you.

ARK: I am more and more aware that I carry an awareness of his presence. And for me at least, acceptance and patience are part of a lifelong journey.

REK: What are the hardest things to accept?

ARK: The death of a patient. There were moments in my professional life when I was confronted, as any doctor would be, with my frailty and the diagnostic and therapeutic limitations of that time. I marvel at the steps forward in the past decades that enable more patients to survive challenging illnesses and complications.

REK: How did you process such a loss?

ARK: I had often developed a relationship with the family, which did not end when the patient died. It was helpful to me, and I hope to them, to be as available to them as I could be, including attending the funeral. I would also lean on fellow caregivers who knew what I was experiencing, and we would help one another.

As an aside, that was what the creation of the Center for Compassion in Medical Care was all about. To allow process to take place. One such form was with Schwartz Rounds, which launched forums to focus on the interaction between caregiver and patients (and caregiver was a loose term to be inclusive of all staff from doctors to housekeepers).

No one can escape that dying is part of the life cycle. This is something that all of us must face. For those who work amid life-and-death circumstances, all the more so.

I remember a young man with intestinal tuberculosis. Anesthesia said he was at risk for surgery. He was suffering. It seemed there was little we could do for him. So, I sat with him through the night he died. I had nothing to give but myself. My presence as a fellow human being was what I could offer.

There was an international visiting professor. His car got sideswiped during a snowstorm. I was able to operate on him, but he died of uncontrolled bleeding. It was very difficult—and like any surgeon, I felt the inadequacy of the moment. I'm not trying to absolve myself, but in those days, we didn't have the diagnostic tools to resolve the quandary.

To be aware that an intervention is necessary, to initiate it and then, because of the limitation of medical knowledge, to know you can only do so much is brutal. It's the difference between life and death. You always want to be able to do something more. Processing a patient's death is the most complicated thing. You take it out and examine it and re-examine it. *V'hafachta Bo...*" *(Hebrew for the beginning of a maxim of Rabbi Ben Bag Bag who says, "Search in it and search in it, since everything is in it. And in it should you look, and grow old and be worn in it; and from it do not move, since there is no characteristic greater than it." from Pirkei Avot, Sayings of the Fathers, 5:22)*

Sometimes there's value in that exercise, but one must guard against doing it as a way to "punish" oneself for not having all the answers.

The *Talmud (a central text of Rabbinic Judaism and the primary source of Jewish religious law and theology)* speaks quite dramatically about the value of saving a life being the equivalent to saving the world.

My dad, *may the memory of the righteous be for a blessing*, used to say to me, when I graduated medical school, "Avram, remember that you are an assistant 'to the True Healer.' *Al tomar (Hebrew for do not say)*, "kohe v'etzem yadee ahsa lee at hahayil hazeh." *(Hebrew for "[only through] the strength of my hand I did this powerful thing" [Isaiah 10:13]).*

This reminder I hold near and dear. I am blessed and humbled to be an assistant to the Divine Being.

So, you develop a heartfelt mantra. It evolves over time, but my internal dialogue sounds something like:

I am blessed with skills that I use to the best of my ability.

Doctors are not G-d and don't have all the answers.

Each day, I ask the Divine Being to guide the work of my hand.

That limited invocation is what I have to lean on.

REK: For the early-career person in a role of service, what's your advice around self-love and self-preservation?

ARK: This is a very personal journey. For some it feels like a calling. And many people are working through their own issues while they're serving. We are all human. In this work, you are the instrument of healing. Your compassion, your intellect, your expertise—all are integrated in service to the patient.

When that's not enough, you ask for help. When you're weary, you seek rest and rejuvenation. That part is probably the most difficult because it can feel impossible and terribly selfish to put your needs before someone else you believe is suffering.

REK: And what about the concept of acceptance of self on the personal front?

ARK: It takes courage to listen to your own voice and do what's right for *you*. Hopefully, each of us finds at least one kindred spirit, romantic or otherwise, who can help you seek balance when you're unsure of your priorities.

Kerana did that for me in the early days of our marriage. We moved back to Boston, my birthplace, for me to serve as Chief Resident at a Boston hospital. I subsequently announced that we needed to start being more observant (more traditional in religious practice) out of respect for my father.

When we first met, we were both rebelling against our traditional Jewish upbringing. Kerana was understandably concerned at the notion that I was proposing changing rules with little notice. She insisted, as is her way, that we simply invite my dad for a discussion and talk it through, explaining that our faith practices were evolving differently from his. And that we did. I shouldn't have been surprised when he said without a change in voice that of course he would prefer that we practice more traditionally, but without hesitation he added, "I will love and accept you, whatever your choice."

There is no question that this was a pivotal moment in my relationship with both my father and my wife, and most importantly, with myself. I cannot say that I never doubted myself again. That is the fiction of storybooks. But I did come to understand myself and my father, and my relationship with my wife a little better, and that is not only very sweet and rewarding, but also an integral part of my personal growth. ✍

....

"Ein d'var ha-omed bifnay haratzon…"

"There is nothing that if you will it,
  that can't be accomplished."

> —*Credited to a variety of sources including the
> Zohar (Vol. 2. P. 162b), the Lubavitcher
> Rebbe Yosef Yitzchak Schneerson and Zionist
> leader Menachem Ussishkin, and quoted
> frequently by Harry Kraft, father of Avram,
> Robert and Elizabeth Kraft*

....

Repairing the World

REK: I've often heard you say how your father loved to make peace, to bring harmony to his home and the world around him. Similarly, I've watched you focus your energies on improving the lives of others in tandem with *Tikkun Olam (Hebrew for the Jewish concept meaning to repair the world with acts of kindness).*

ARK: Yes, my father's dictum of giving to others became my own: *"ahavat shalom bain adam l'rayahu" (Hebrew for making peace among people).* He was committed daily to *gemilut chasadim (Hebrew for acts of loving kindness).* He taught his three children an essential lesson on the importance of choosing goodness: the value of harnessing your will to do good in the world. In my way of thinking, this was his greatest gift to us. The way he lived his life and doing good were synchronous.

My grandfather used to say of his son Aaron, my father's biblical name, that Harry emulated the behavior of the biblical Aaron, *"ohave shalom, v'rodef shalom, ohave et habriot umkurvan latorah" (Hebrew for "he loved peace, he pursued peace, he loved G-d's creatures and brought them closer to the Torah" —from Pirkei Avot, Sayings of the Fathers, 1:12).*

There's a certain grandeur that elevates our state of being from solely serving one person and aligning what is ours with something that's as big as the world. I don't wholly understand what that peace meant to him. I think it had many layers. Surely his intent was to bring harmony into his home and at the same time, to the outside world.

The mandate of *Tikkun Olam (Hebrew for repairing the world)* was ever present in our home and something that

I've always embraced wholeheartedly. Simply put, it places the responsibility of making our world better in each of our hands.

In the Jewish tradition, vessels of divine light were shattered in the evolution of creation in order to permit free will. The art of our human condition is to gather *shevirat ha-kelim (Hebrew for the breaking of the vessels that contain G-d's light)* in the form of *Tikkun Olam (Hebrew for repairing the world).* If we accept that through the release of G-d's light there is the freedom to choose what will occur and that gathering the light repairs the world, then we're recognizing the power of choosing good or bad. The same with words. They can both hurt and heal. It's our choice to match words to G-d's creativity and repair our injured world.

And to be open to that charge, one must first find your own sense of balance before you can share good with others and hopefully, through your actions, encourage them to do the same. Our internal harmony is critical to choosing our path well. And when we find that we're challenged, we must find a way to cultivate our equilibrium.

Let me give a personal example. We were living in Columbus, Ohio, and I was doing my residency. I was overwhelmed. My brilliant chief of surgery was tough, and that's an understatement. And from time to time, I struggled with the existential question: "Is this how and where I want to direct my life's work?" It was the strong counsel of my brother, channeling our father, who brought to bear *"Ein d'var ha'omad bifnai harazon"* (Hebrew for *"There is nothing that if you will it, that can't be accomplished"*).

Rob saw my medical path as my translation of how to live out my dream as a healer instead of, say, serving as a *rabbi* or a social worker. Tapping into the trusted counsel of a neutral party can be stabilizing, which we all need during personal crises.

With the benefit of so many decades behind me, I have a deepening understanding of how our actions, even seemingly small and unintentional, can benefit those around us. We *can* make an impact.

REK: What responsibility do we have for one another?

ARK: Every day, we have an opportunity to make an impact on one another. What we have will be fleeting, as a dream, if you don't care about yourself and the next person. You are only as good as what you bring to the table and not what you remove from it.

Improving the lives of others—isn't that the foundation for peace as healing? Not just creating the healthiest internal environment for the self, but extending that energy to the sphere of the outside world.

REK: Besides your parents' impact, what other factors set you on your path?

ARK: Our family friend Moshe Lieberman probably never knew the profound impact he had on my life. Not only did he gently steer me toward a career in medicine, but in my early years, it was his constant and generous belief in me that pushed me to achieve and perhaps believe a little more in myself.

I was the youngest kid in our Hebrew school class and definitely not the smartest. But years later, because of his faith in me, I actually was given the honor of serving as valedictorian of our Hebrew school. His influence also allowed me to give that valedictorian speech in Hebrew, and his strong faith has lived on in me for many years.

Moshe had a strong Jewish background, was open to modern biblical criticism and was worthy of the trust people put in him as a technician of text. He was technically capable of working out the complexities of biblical material. He had enough confidence to give me an impetus to want to study with greater intent, which was probably the stepping stone I needed at that time to preserve what was then just the beginning to my questions and search for meaning. So, his mentorship was incalculable.

REK: Your humility may keep you from realizing that you, too, have played that important a role for others.

ARK: That would be a blessing if it were even partly true. On occasion, a former colleague will reach out and share that I've made a difference to them, in some fashion, which is always a humbling experience. I remember one in particular, from a collaborator and friend who expressed gratitude for my influence. He said I expressed confidence and faith in him when he had little of his own. He wrote that the respect of an esteemed associate ultimately allowed him to have greater faith in his own talents. I had no idea in all our years of working together that he was ever anything but fully self-assured. And the impact of his note on me made me ever more conscious of sharing with others when their words and actions made a difference to me.

I am constantly reminded how we have endless opportunities to show we care, to make a difference in seemingly small ways that ripple across the years growing more impactful in time and in ways that have the potential of repairing the world.

REK: Is part of repairing the world repairing yourself?

ARK: Yes, of course, and that can be the most challenging of all.

I've spent the last 60 years realizing that there is nothing wrong with becoming enmeshed in other people's lives, sharing intimate moments of vulnerability, recognizing suffering and trying to alleviate it.

At my own low points, I have on occasion found it difficult to look past my own despair and be of service to others. Thank goodness for the many who extended a hand to me when I was in need.

In 1975, the man who played unquestionably the largest role in my life departed this world. When I got the call that my father was hospitalized with a heart attack, I was off to Boston as quickly as I could get on a plane. At age 40, with almost childlike naiveté, I was praying that maybe at 30,000 feet my prayers would reach the Divine Being more quickly. My father, my personal hero, died when I was climbing in altitude to be with him. And that yearning for his proximity has remained an intimate companion. I was distraught.

And I shared that deep sense of loss with my brother and sister. I am so grateful for the closeness of my siblings Rob and Lee Lee. Our mutual love and support sustained me, and I can't imagine how lonely it would have felt to have mourned our father, and then one day our mother, without them.

Ultimately, the power of faith, tradition and love helped me find my way back. I discovered a lifeline in the recitation of a prayer I had known my entire life. *"V'ahavta et Hashem Elochecha bekhol levavavkha u'vekhol nafshekha u'vekhol me'odekha" (Hebrew for "And you shall love the Lord, your God, with all of your heart, soul and might...from the prayer "The Shema," Deuteronomy 6:4-5).*

As for me, it was as if I had never heard these words before, a new and healing balm for my soul and a way to find meaning in my personal loss. I knew I had to go on living, loving and in my own small way trying to repair the world without my father's physical presence. ✍

"Whoever destroys a soul, it is considered as if he destroyed an entire world. And whoever saves a life, it is considered as if he saved an entire world."

—*The Yerushalmi Talmud, Tractate Sanhedrin 37a, the Talmud is a collection of writings that is about both Jewish law and Jewish tradition*

Majesty of the Unknown

REK: The spiritual world has always spoken to you. Does it have a place in a life of service?

ARK: Surely. Both blend into the essence of my being and augment my mindfulness. In the spiritual world, I am not limited by a faith system. Beyond my Judaism, I also find inspiration from the Eastern traditions, Christianity and Islam. I am captivated by Rumi, the Sufi mystic/Persian poet who says, "Grief can be the garden of compassion. If you keep your heart open through everything, your pain can become your greatest ally in your life's search for love and wisdom."

As I studied to be a doctor, I busied myself with the facts of medicine. I would catch myself discounting the "coincidences" that can appear in a day that might hold internal or mystical meaning. For me, those moments can be mined for inspiration and lessons and can provide profound guidance to the open mind, heart and soul of the unfettered student.

On waking, I say a prayer of thanksgiving, to be open and grateful to *G-d's presence*. My daily prayer began with:

Modeh ani lifanekha melekh chai v'kayam shehechezarta bi nishmahti b'chemlah, rabah emunatekha (Hebrew for "I give thanks before you, living and eternal King, for You have returned within me my soul with compassion; abundant is Your faithfulness!")

And, during the holiday of Thanksgiving, I would recite *M'zmor L'todah (Hebrew for "A Psalm of Thanksgiving"):*

"Make a joyful noise unto the LORD, all ye lands. Serve the LORD with gladness: come before His presence with singing. Know ye that the LORD He is G-d: it is He that hath made us, and not we ourselves; we are His people, and the sheep of His pasture. Enter into His gates with thanksgiving, and into His courts with praise: be thankful unto Him, and bless His name. For the LORD is good; His mercy is everlasting; and His truth endureth to all generations." —Psalm 100

What began as an annual prayer has now become a daily practice, and this Psalm in particular has become one of the elements in fulfilling my search for enhancing the "I-thou relationship" with G-d (Martin Buber).

Part of my daily practices is reminding myself to be open to the mysterious ways a day can unfold.

REK: Tell me about such a day.

ARK: Let's begin with a stroll. Kerana and I were trekking by the ocean in Southern Florida. It was a February morning— nothing compared to the weather at our home in Chicago but still brisk for Florida and also refreshing. We had set off for a short outing, but for some inexplicable reason we decided to keep going.

So, we crossed to the shore side of the road, walking towards a rise capped with a cupola structure, and could see that sitting under this umbrella was a man of sizable physical presence reading a book. He was wearing a football cap with the emblem of the New England Patriots football team.

I must digress here for a moment to add that Kerana and I have had many special encounters in our life because of her capacity to engage with those around her. She knows it made me uncomfortable in the beginning, but I watch and learn how she asks questions and engages people in their story. Now I can include those skills in my arsenal.

As we approached the man, he smiled in a welcoming manner. I could not resist saying to him, "What a great Patriots season." One comment led to another and before long, the three of us were engaged in a shared conversation about our hopes, life choices and beliefs.

Kerana, noting the man's physical stature, asked if he had been a football player. "Yes," he responded in an unassuming way. He had played for the Patriots in the '70s, under Chuck Fairbanks, at a rough-and-tough time in the history of professional football. He acknowledged that a vicious attempt on his life led him to a new profession, distant from his playing career, that actualized his spiritual strength. Due to that experience, he "found" his inner self and came to know that his next mission was to do G-d's purpose focused on repairing and not on destroying.

He described his current commitment to a healing ministry with fellow athletes like Reggie White of the Green Bay Packers. Their service reached out to inner-city kids and penitentiary inmates, helping them find their inner selves and individual spirituality. In passing, he mentioned that he would be in Massachusetts in a few weeks at the Walpole prison together with the Patriots' Curtis Martin. Maybe, he said, he hoped he'd have the chance to meet the club's new owner, Robert Kraft.

REK: This work of his sounds aligned with your personal dedication to *Tikkun Olam (Hebrew for repairing the world).*

ARK: Exactly. And this committed Christian was telling us about his nonjudgmental experience of another person's belief system. For him, there was an inner force urging him to teach a personal message stimulated from a divine source—that there was more on this earth than acquiring possessions.

REK: All from an "innocent" walk on the beach!

ARK: Kerana asked if he had any "hate in his heart" for what had happened to him in the attack on his life. He quoted scriptures for his response: "Vengeance is (only) mine, sayeth the Lord" (Deuteronomy 32:35 and see the New Testament iteration in Romans 12:19). I also recognized that theme from the *Torah* in the book of Leviticus. I remarked that our father *of blessed memory* had taught our family another biblical verse for a similar spiritual lesson regarding the exercise of power and spirituality. He quoted: "Don't say, 'It is *my* strength and the power of *my* hand that made me victorious,' but rather understand that your energy has a divine source."

REK: How powerful to be able to share such heartfelt messages with a stranger on the beach!

ARK: We were oblivious to how cool it was outside. The conversation was warming us. Our dialogue shifted to a conversation about the individual ability to affect people whom we encounter. Kerana, a practicing nurse, told us that she personally doubted her individual ability to impact her patients in a spiritual dimension.

This retired Patriots player—now a faith minister—responded to her in the following way: "I make myself vulnerable by sharing my pain with others who suffer." He continued quietly and sensitively. "Though I am physically a strong man, I can't bear to see the ill suffer. But together we can share this load. This is our ministry, this wonderful opportunity to heal—when a person is psychologically fragile and spiritually needing. Maybe you just don't know you're doing it yet."

As I recall this, I think for me, when there's an absence of a spiritual dimension, there's a feeling as if you're entering a vacuum and that spiritual energy has just been sucked out.

REK: You're always reminding us that we often don't know the impact we can have on people.

ARK: It was time for us to go our separate ways. He paused, looked out at the sea and then at us. He said, "When I went out this morning, I said to my wife, 'I wonder what the Lord has in store for me today'…and look what's happened." We shook hands and finally, after talking so personally, we exchanged our names.

REK: And…

ARK: His name was Art Moore. He proudly wore the number 75 on his Patriots jersey.

We introduced ourselves as Avram and Kerana Kraft. He casually inquired with a faint smile if we were any relation of the owner of the Patriots. "Yes," I said. "Robert is my brother." His jaw literally dropped. "You're *kidding* me? You're *teasing* me?" We assured him that we weren't. "I've heard good things about your brother." I smiled for my brother's many worldly accomplishments.

Before parting, he wrote a message to me on a piece of paper. I didn't read it until we were on the road back to the hotel. He had written his name, his wife's name and "Jesus loves you."

REK: A blessing.

ARK: A "Moore" blessing…that was how I experienced it, too. I don't have to be a Christian to be deeply affected by Art's belief in the healing power of love in this world of strife and bitterness and his commitment to giving *more* of himself.

REK: You were open to what the day brought.

ARK: That's what I'm talking about. Too often we walk with our shoulders up and head down, bracing against the day. I know because I've caught myself doing that so many times. But if we stand up, shoulders back, face forward and remain open — not always an easy task when we perceive the world's weight is on us — it can be amazing what the day brings. Sometimes it can be a chance meeting. Sometimes it can be a spiritual intervention. And it can be a little of both, depending on your individual orientation.

REK: Tell me about one that is of a more spiritual nature.

ARK: The mystical presence of those who have gone before us is very real to me. A force in my life. I think the awareness of their energy provides me strength. It's a matter of being open to the possibility that the universe has something to share with you, including energy from those no longer physically of this earth.

In 1985, Kerana and I went to Israel and stayed with our friends Bernie and Fran Alpert who had made *Aliyah (Hebrew meaning ascent—in addition to referring to the move from outside of Israel to live in Israel, it also refers to chanting the blessings before and after reading the Torah).* They lived in Jerusalem's Jewish Quarter. They were accomplished tour guides and gave us a whirlwind experience traveling from the Golan Heights to the Red Sea, and East Jerusalem to Haifa with many stops at ancient and significant archaeological sites along the way.

Those were heady days, and we cherished the immersive experience in the land of our forebears. It was our first trip to the Holy Land, and it was a decade after my father had died, a holy man in my mind. To keep him close, I wore his (and that of his father before him) *tefillin* (a set of small black leather boxes containing scrolls of parchment inscribed with verses from the *Torah*) during prayer. We went to all sorts of prayer services around the city and at the West Bank, culminating with participation in prayer at the *Kotel* (the Western Wall of the ancient temple).

While I enjoyed each moment, I would be disingenuous if I didn't admit that I was waiting for a thunderbolt from the heavens, a communication from beyond. Sadly, I experienced no such occurrence.

REK: A real disappointment.

ARK: We were in the land of milk and honey. I was anticipating all sorts of magical moments. On our last *Shabbat (Hebrew for Sabbath)* in Jerusalem, Kerana and I were standing on the parapet overlooking the *Kotel* Plaza. There were throngs of people hurrying down the steps to pray at the Western Wall, and someone called out from the surging crowd: "Aren't you Rachel Kraft's parents?"

How remarkable to be picked out of a crowd this way, so far from home, in Jerusalem of all places. They introduced themselves as parents of your dear camp friend Marla, from Kansas City, Missouri, and said they recognized us from our family photo on our annual Jewish New Year card that happened to be taped to their refrigerator. And, as if this were not enough of a sign to alert me to the holiness of this time and place, there was more to come.

I was reluctant to leave this site. The pull to stay and engage was strong. Kerana sensed that and urged me to join a group of students marching to the *Kotel (Hebrew for the ancient retaining limestone wall in the Old City of Jerusalem also known as the Western Wall)* to pray. They were singing and rounding a bend when suddenly the afternoon prayer service began. Though I knew the prayers from memory, I still wanted a *siddur (Hebrew for prayer book)* so I wouldn't make a mistake. The man next to me held out his prayer book for us to share, and amazingly, he was a neurologist I knew from Chicago. The world continued to feel intimate and joyful. The chanting elevated, and I was fully in the moment before the service ended far too quickly for me. Suddenly the crowd dispersed.

REK: And you and Mom?

ARK: Kerana and I found each other and walked happily back to the Alperts' home in the Jewish Quarter to join them at their *Shabbat* table. As was our custom, we all stood and surrounded the beautifully appointed table, held hands and began chanting the song sung by traditional Jews on Friday night upon returning home from the synagogue. Singing *"Shalom Aleichem" (Hebrew for "Peace be unto you")* was a ritual for me since childhood. The melody sung by Jews around the world ushers in a celebratory mood for the Sabbath.

To be in the moment as I did each *Shabbat*, I closed my eyes and swayed and sang with everyone around what my dad called the "family board," the gathering of those near and dear around a communal table. The blessing from the biblical book of *Bemidbar (Hebrew name for* Numbers 6:24-27) engenders love and peace:

> *Peace be upon you, O angels who serve G-d, angels of the Most High—from the King who is above all other kings, the Holy One, Blessed is G-d.*

> *Come in peace, O angels of peace, angels of the Most High—from the King who is above all other kings, the Holy One, Blessed is G-d.*

> *Bless me with peace, O angels of peace, angels of the Most High—from the King who is above all other kings, the Holy One, Blessed is G-d.*

Depart in peace, O angels of peace, angels of the Most High—from the King who is above all other kings, the Holy One, Blessed is G-d.

In that moment as I sang with my eyes closed, I witnessed a vision of my space changing; I was at the threshold of a dark tunnel, the far end of which was illuminated with shimmering dancing figures. It was at that instant, as our chant concluded, that I felt a tap on my right shoulder. It was gentle, but awakening because I had been in another place. I opened my eyes and saw us still standing hand in hand. Intuitively, I knew it was my father *of blessed memory* who had been present and was tangibly telling me he was there with me in this moment and affirming that I was in the right place at the right time. I believe he was giving me his blessing that was abiding and filled with peace and love that found a place in my heart and soul forever.

This powerful, mystical memory is one I recall every *Erev Shabbat (Hebrew for the eve of the Sabbath)* when I extend the very same blessing to my wife and children.

REK: Some find the mystical uncomfortable, unnerving or even a figment of the imagination.

ARK: Yes, I understand. For me, this has been a process of experience and acceptance. I am grateful when I'm open enough to be the recipient of such a message.

REK: I once read in a Unity Church newsletter that we can see coincidences as coincidences or little miracles. It's our choice.

ARK: When we're closed off to the majesty of the unknown, our world can get very closed in. I've had my own dark periods and am grateful to Kerana for encouraging me to remain engaged and connected with something bigger than myself. I can think of a number of incidents when I found my way back through song, study and community.

One was after back surgery a few years ago. When I awoke from the aftermath of anesthetics and various meds, I really wasn't sure that I was the same person who went to sleep before the anesthetic.

I emerged confused and disoriented, and my condition necessitated a few days' stay in the hospital's ICU.

When my wounds were healing nicely and I was ambulatory, though fatigued, I was discharged from the hospital. It was as if I were two different people. An ordinary soul before and a depleted, lost being after. I felt the impact of this life event, and its physiological demands had depleted me and I needed to be recharged. It was as if I had a psychological need for a revitalizing. Like energy being sapped and needing to be infused. For me, being reconnected to a vital source of mystical charge helped immensely.

It was early fall, and we were moving from the *Days of Awe* between *Rosh Hashanah* and *Yom Kippur* to the celebration of *Sukkot*. It serves to remind us of the frailty and brevity of life. It was a transition from a physical place to a spiritual pilgrimage.

At the time, I leaned on a Psalm of Thanksgiving. I had made it to this season, and I was grateful but also felt a darkness. My study partner David suggested we ease into the day's text by first immersing ourselves in a *Chassidic (ultra-orthodox branch of Judaism) nigun (Hebrew for melody)* to get into the "right space."

We did. I reached for my *tallis (Hebrew for prayer shawl)* and enveloped myself while we listened to the CD. I found myself crying in a very natural way. Rabbi Joe Schultz, our study leader these past four years, likened the experience to a bud unfolding into a flower. I had never had that experience before and found it cleansing. Again, an openness to move outside of myself, letting song, study and community transport myself out, above and beyond. ✍

....

"A coincidence is a small miracle when God
chooses to remain anonymous."

— *Albert Einstein, Nobel Prize-winning
physicist who developed the theory of relativity,
one of the two pillars of modern physics.*

....

Seeking Joy

REK: Talk to me about the concept of joy in your life.

ARK: I believe in Rebbe Nachman's principle that states: "There is a great commandment to be in a state of joy always." That joy is an extension of our love for G-d and our gratitude for this life and the many gifts of each day.

Similarly, one of my father's principles was: "There's nothing so bad there isn't some good in it."

For me, participating in religious ceremonies and ritual has been a great source of joy. I wish that I had an easier time accessing that level of joy and celebratory energy in day-to-day activities. I marvel at Kerana's capacity for enjoyment and her almost childlike wonder, finding delight in the world around her. I've struggled with feelings of guilt when I experience joy or pleasure because it makes me feel unworthy when there's so much to do in the world.

REK: Tell me more.

ARK: I've developed a better sense of self-awareness in my later years that it can't just be about being "a good person." Yes, every day I can strive to be of service—but if I am a vessel for the Divine, then my daily goal must include an equal measure of celebrating all that is joyous, and similarly all that is *not* joyous. My family and community must know they can engage with me, and that vital connection to them is what fuels my work in the field of healing.

REK: A theme of Rabbi Nachman's.

ARK: This state of mind that Nachman defines so clearly as being essential for personal growth requires some special notation to understand who the man was. He himself was a miracle, and surely what he brought into the world expanded the creation of a movement that his great-grandfather founded.

Specifically, Nachman suffered greatly in his abbreviated life. He died of tuberculosis at a young age, and four of his children died in infancy. Nachman became profoundly depressed, and he worked assiduously at establishing meaning in the losses he experiences.

At a personal level, I am overwhelmed at the energy he had to conjure to maintain a worldly sense of balance in the face of the privation he had to live through. I find it a great inspiration/wonder for any of us who have suffered loss and maintained the integrity of self.

REK: How do you find your way to joy?

ARK: Music is a way for me to access great joy. I'm able to lose myself in singing, particularly joining voices with others, sharing the experience with others. It has always been a way for me to feel part of a community. In fact, early on when we moved to Highland Park and were invited to the home of our now dear friends Fran and Bernie (whom we would subsequently visit in Israel), singing at the Sabbath dinner played a pivotal role for me in finding a sense of ease, comfort and belonging.

When we first moved to town, truthfully, I was not interested in accepting the invitation from these strangers. Without the prodding and insistence from Kerana, I likely would have stayed home. While initially reticent and, if I am honest, uncomfortable, when I heard the familiar melody of *Shabbat* songs, I felt I was home. Sharing the tradition, the melodies and what I innately understood to be a caring community brought me great joy.

REK: I've heard from many people that you are a force in bringing and keeping community together.

ARK: I have immense gratitude for the community that has played such a significant role in my life. I must acknowledge that I sometimes look at life through a black crepe, and I've had to consciously and with great effort pull the drapes aside to see the true light around me. Cultivating gratitude is now one of my tools to access joy.

There's a danger in today's world, in the richness and complexity of our society, to take too much for granted. Miraculous advances in medicine and science have made treatment and recovery almost a given. But for me, in my own ongoing "recovery," there are numerous gifts to be celebrated. I hope with gratitude I will continue to experience the wonders and miracles in the newness of each day.

REK: But sometimes we're challenged, and the joy doesn't feel accessible.

ARK: The world around us is full of reminders to open our eyes and hearts, sometimes when we need it most. On a visit to Boston to see my mom *of blessed memory* near the end of her life, I witnessed an extraordinary display of joy Just outside her hospital room as I wandered lost in my own thoughts.

On this magnificent spring-like winter day, I saw a hospital employee step outside with arms raised reciting, "This is the day that the Lord has made, let us be happy and rejoice in it."

This statement from Psalms (118:24) was immediately recognizable to me and jolted me into real presence, and toward the joy of the day.

We would soon lose our mum to this green earth, but now I remember her final days co-mingled with the memory of "This *is* the day that the Lord has made, let us be happy and rejoice in it." ✍

....

"It is good to set aside a specific time every day
to be heartbroken and to speak out all one's problems
before God, but the rest of the day be only happy."

*—Rabbi Nachman of Breslov, one of the most
creative and influential Chassidic rabbis and
founder of the Breslov Chassidic sect*

....

Finding Balance

REK: The tension around work/life balance is very prevalent today in mainstream media and cultural conversation. What is *your* approach?

ARK: Finding balance is hard fought for so many of us. In the *Chassidic* tradition, a priority is placed on making balance in your life and creating an environment that encourages the worthiness of being in a state of balance. The thinking is that this allows you to be in a more spiritually secure internal space because with balance comes holiness.

REK: Tell me what that means, "with balance comes holiness."

ARK: Balance induces a state of proximity to the Divine. Balance for me relates to harmony with this world and those closest to us. For me, it's when the forces in my world align and I'm listening to what I need and open to what I can give to others.

REK: A state of grace?

ARK: Yes. Grace in the Hebrew sense is translated from the words "loving kindness." Self-love—a challenge for many, myself included—is necessary for finding this state of balance. The ideal is to know that in a world of chaos, there are positive and negative forces, and we are all a reflection of that. It's about trying to find an internal state of peace by utilizing the divine energy in each of us—a work in progress, to be sure.

REK: And how does one access the divine energy in each of us?

ARK: That's a very personal path. For me, it comes in many forms—through prayer, song, voices in harmony, being with family, study, slowing down to enjoy the sun on my face. But a big piece is slowing down, being present so that one can hear what people are saying and what they're *not* saying, and to cultivate through it a personal equilibrium.

REK: Balance is so critical to well-being. A loss of balance for caregivers could be dangerous I would think.

ARK: Indeed, and I have witnessed that both professionally and personally. While there's no limit to divine goodness, there are limits to human energy, time and fortitude. Today, the phrase is "compassion fatigue." And philosophically it gives me pause to imagine being too tired to be compassionate—but in reality, it's far too common.

My own father was so fully available to his community in which he was so beloved that his level of devotion meant time away from family, let alone time for self-care. Without conscious realization, I repeated a similar pattern. My dedication to my patients left me with less energy for my own family, and also for myself.

REK: Do you feel you ever figured out how to break the cycle and achieve the balance that allowed you to give without stripping yourself of what you need to be healthy?

ARK: For anyone engaged in the work of service—which could be a professional caregiver or someone caring for a child or a parent—finding balance is essential. Imagine all that is sacrificed if you're too tired, too weary and too closed off to be present for someone in need. And yet that is the state in which many of us find ourselves. I wish I could say I solved this during my practice career, but like many fellow travelers, I struggled with this throughout my lifetime.

What I learned, though, is that you'll catch yourself saying I'll take care of myself "when..." and *that's* the danger moment. When your body or mind signals "I need a break," that's the moment to listen in the way you would to the wail of a baby or the cry of a child. To ignore those internal pleas for self-help may be understood as self-sabotage.

REK: In medicine, there are tales of residents working 24-hour shifts. What would you say to them?

ARK: Thankfully, that's changing, and they're protected from those kinds of hours, which is better for them and for the patients. As a backup system, each of us would be wise to identify our own "personal guardian." Maybe that's a spouse, significant other, parent, sibling or friend. We must trust that person enough that when they say "enough," we listen. Because when you're caught up in the action plan of your engagement and the adrenalin of being in service, it can be very difficult to hit the off button.

Finding balance continues to be my task. I've been searching to understand myself better my whole professional life and trust I have made at least modest strides in finding the ever-elusive "balance."

Cultivating balance is a lifelong effort!

It's a matter of presence, of patience and of open, unbiased listening.

This open pathway to learning can also be the portal to balance. ✍

"Your hand opens and closes and opens and closes. If it were always a fist or always stretched open, you would be paralyzed. Your deepest presence is in every small contracting and expanding, the two as beautifully balanced and coordinated as bird wings."

—*Rumi, Sufi mystic, Persian poet*

Standing on
Their Shoulders

REK: You talk a great deal about those who came before you. You also talk about the students and patients from whom you've learned.

ARK: So many people provided me with a strong foundation to build a good life for myself. My father gave me an introduction and application to our heritage that was rich beyond measure. His father used to compare him to the biblical Aaron for whom he was named— *"ohave shalom, v'rodef shalom, ohave et habriot umkurvan latorah," "He loved peace, he pursued peace, he loved G-d's creatures and brought them closer to the study of Torah"* —from *Pirkei Avot 1:12, Sayings of the Fathers* —part of Jewish ethical literature.

Honoring his memory by trying to help "repair the world" helps me celebrate his life as the most influential person in my life.

I yearn to learn, and that hunger is sustaining. I've spoken of my seminal teachers Egon Lewin and Moshe Lieberman. Today, that person is Rabbi Joe Schultz, who 50 years ago was the *m'sader kiddushin (Hebrew for marriage officiant)* for our marriage ceremony.

REK: Was it not Rabbi Schultz who reignited your learning at a time when you were feeling lost?

ARK: Yes. I was having a dark patch three years ago and received a call from Joe Schultz. He told me he had a dream. He also said he wanted to tell me about it in person. It was a few weeks before we were able to be together. I ended up meeting with Joe when our immediate family visited our Boston family for the *Pesach (Hebrew for Passover) siddarim (Hebrew for seders).*

Joe knew from family members that I was having a hard time. When we met at synagogue, he took me aside and told me that he had a dream in which his father *of blessed memory* said that I, Avram, should become a *rabbi*. Joe interpreted this dream at a personal level. He understood the meaning as his call was meant to train me for *semicha (Hebrew for becoming a rabbi),* which he envisioned as my path through this acute depression.

Candidly, I did not believe I was intended for the *rabbinate (Hebrew for the collective institution of rabbis),* but I did warm to the idea of studying with Joe joined by my longtime study partner David.

REK: Both studying and teaching have been important to you. While preparing for our conversation, I came across a gift from residents you taught who presented you with a book with the following inscription: "To Avram Kraft whose scholarship, clinical judgment, technical skills and humanity have helped shape our careers in medicine." What did you learn from *your* students?

ARK: I learned from my students curiosity, good humor and humanity. These were the elements that drew us together as a "family" unit.

I also learned from anyone around me who took the time to truly look at what life presented them. None more visibly than Bertie Lochlear, the housekeeper for our surgical resident on-call room during our five years at Ohio State

University in Columbus. Our supervisor, the Head of Surgery, would refer to her often to illustrate someone totally attentive to people's bodily needs as instruction to us to look at everyone thoughtfully, carefully and respectfully.

We need to be in awe, daily. May we be ever mindful, especially in our proffering wisdom to the next generation, to rein in our ego, to give honor to our life guides and to give thanks to those who hoisted us on their shoulders. May we always carry our burden with dignity and hand it off with equanimity.

REK: You were invited to teach students about the importance of these principles.

ARK: There was a technique that I chose to employ in teaching medical students and residents in which I did role-playing and where I assumed the posture of pretense of the attending physician who was a know-it-all and while lumbering to the bedside, dragging a chair that was otherwise meant for the family, plopping down on the seat and uncovering the patient indelicately. I would arbitrarily criticize, and I did it on purpose to provoke the viewers of this interaction as to what's wrong with this scene. What don't you like about what you're witnessing? There was some giggling because they were not accustomed to learning in this unfamiliar environment—a topsy-turvy element seeing their teacher assume a different role. ℘

....

"Live as if you were to die tomorrow.
Learn as if you were to live forever."

—*Mahatma Gandhi, an Indian activist who
led India to independence against British rule
employing nonviolent civil disobedience*

....

Listening Versus Hearing

REK: Tell me what you think are the essential elements in the healing process.

ARK: Healing is a shared adventure. It's a multi-factorial, miraculous process. Can you imagine a surgeon visualizing a diseased portion of the intestine, resected, reconnected surgically and within a time interval uniting and propagating intestinal contents and their being totally functional? It is a physical miracle.

Healing requires co-participation. It requires an urgent intervention, a motivated patient, a response that's timely, an interval that's immeasurable, and a mystical process, measured as a physical event.

It is an imperative.

Caregiving is not just a "cookie cutter" event. It requires acute sensitivity to the person in front of you.

I can remember a time when I was on the receiving end of such care myself, in an unexpected way.

When I was a Chief Resident at Beth Israel, I received a call from The Hebrew Home, a nursing home in Boston. One of their patients needed urgent surgery for an obstructing colon tumor. I met the patient in the Emergency Department. I was thunderstruck. He was our dear family friend Moshe Lieberman.

I approached my Surgical Supervisor Don Glotzer and told him that the patient was not only an early mentor of mine, but my adopted grandfather who required urgent surgical intervention and that I was incapable of operating on this "family member." Don listened and said, "Admit him to my service and I'll take care of him *with* you." Outside of the operating room, he continued, "Why don't you prepare him and then I'll scrub in and take over." Perhaps I shouldn't have been surprised when in the OR he added, "*You* are going to be the operating surgeon and *I'm* going to assist *you*." And that indeed is what happened.

REK: And how did you feel?

ARK: Don had heard the words I said, and he was truly listening. He intuited that this was a pivotal moment for me. He recognized that I didn't need to shy away from this challenge. By his coaxing me forward, I was able to confront an intimidating and emotional moment and also give to Moshe in the way I had been trained, thus in my mind, giving back to someone who had given so much to me.

Moshe survived the operation and hospitalization and returned to The Hebrew Home following an uncomplicated recovery. It was beyond powerful to me to have played a central role in this man's healing, the same person who guided me into medicine. Was this a coincidence? It doesn't feel that way to me but rather the intention of the Divine. Another miracle in my life.

Moshe was more than a teacher. He was a philosophical visionary and a strong supporter of mine. He listened to me as a youngster and then adolescent, perhaps allowing for his ability to recommend my future life's path in caregiving, and not the *rabbinate*, which my father wished for me.

Listening and really seeing the true other is a vital part of service aligned with healing. Our giving is best expressed if we understand the next person's needs.

Learning life lessons can occur for anyone, from anyone and anywhere. It's a matter of presence, of patience, and of unbiased, unfettered listening. And then, there is also the matter of internal listening.

Since my second stroke this past December, I've been sensitized to certain deficits around making sense of abstract thoughts and sequencing—the logical linking of information. It makes movie and TV watching along with reading, which I love, that much more challenging. I'm frustrated by my lack of recall and my limited patience with myself.

And at a very personal level, I'm having difficulty with personal prayer. The latter has to do with internal tension of wanting to express myself in a prayer mode but feeling restricted by word recall. Thoughts become jumbled, and I'm challenged in making my inner feelings known both to G-d and to myself. It's like relearning about my life and making myself understood. Hopefully with continued effort and patience, I will experience improvement.

Paraphrasing Rabbi Joseph Ber Soloveitchik, prayer doesn't need to be word-based but instead can be intuitive awareness of a prayerful moment. A higher level of cognitive recognition, akin to the overpowering feeling of peace and reverence one feels visualizing the sun rising or setting, storm clouds over a body of water or a mountainous range.

REK: What an exercise in living in the moment.

ARK: After a stroke, there can be attempts of insulating oneself from interactions with people because perhaps you're going to stumble over word usage, your cognitive awareness may be tempered or slowed down, your motor movement may be compromised. To be self-protective is not an uncommon event for the post-stroke patient.

REK: And I sense you're talking about yourself.

ARK: I still am mystified by the beauty of a spring day, the mystical quality of music, the artistic appearance of physical forms…may it never cease. It is an acute feeling of applying the senses to the moment and recognizing that there's something of a higher quality than just seeing, smelling, hearing, tasting, touching. Honoring the voices inside that are demanding to be heard. There is an urgency to the moment.

Post stroke, I'm experiencing that deficit of not being able to fully communicate what I'm experiencing. And because we were not put on this earth to be alone—even prayer is considered elevated if you do it as part of a *minyan (Hebrew for "to be counted" and refers to a gathering of at least 10 people for a prayer service—in a more traditional setting, it would be 10 men)*—I want to end this part of our conversation with a story about "paying attention."

My medical team encouraged me to get out and engage with people outside of my family and care providers. One opportunity was to participate in an annual tradition with my friend Bernie and our fellow congregant Rachel Ferber to visit local nursing homes so that Bernie could blow the *shofar (Hebrew for a ram's horn trumpet sounded during Rosh Hashanah and Yom Kippur)*, a Jewish holiday obligation of the *Torah* for those who may not be able to hear the *shofar* blown in synagogue during the *High Holidays.* During these visits, it's not uncommon for us to interact with 100 or more residents.

There are those who feel uncomfortable with the aging process and the elderly.

Perhaps this is fear of being in their shoes one day, or the demands of being patient. During this annual visit, I'm strongly reminded of what I receive from this wonderful population. We are present for them and in turn receive many gifts. I say to myself, 'Here I am, teach me about what it's going to be like' and I experienced:

> A smile fleetingly swept across the face of a woman we've known and loved for decades who has suffered from longstanding dementia.

> A congregant from our synagogue wept openly that we had thought to visit her.

> A previously mute patient responded to us with single-word answers.

It touched me that individual patients *and* workers were interested in learning and asked questions about these rituals in English, Hebrew and Yiddish. There were moments of *shlaimut (Hebrew for wholeness)* and bonding.

REK: Adam has often said how he loves to watch you interact with older people. Helping them on and off the *bimah (Hebrew for pulpit)*. Your care for and focus on any frail individual.

ARK: That feels like a true *dor l' dor (literally means generation to generation in Hebrew)* statement since I see how Adam intuitively knows how to reach out to those senior members of our family and community.

And what does one do? With Bernie and Rachel, we gave a little of our time. We slowed down to visit. We offered a squeeze of a hand if someone was receptive and a song when one was requested. We listened, and I suspect we were the ones who walked away the richer for it. Listening may take concentration and patience, but it can also fill the listener with unexpected energy and purpose. ✍

....

"You matter because you are you, and you matter
to the end of your life. We will do all we can
not only to help you die peacefully, but also to live
until you die."

> —*Dame Cicely Saunders,*
> *founder of the hospice movement*

....

Sharing Stories

REK: We talk a lot about the impact of stories.

ARK: One person can "give" intangibly and profoundly to another. The only requirement is each being available to another. Stories create such a path.

Around the time of what would have been my father's 93rd birthday, a contemporary of mine, Barry Shrage, reached out to share his own remembrances of growing up in a community with Harry Kraft.

What made that statement even more powerful was that at the time, he also related the following story: It was during the Jewish *High Holidays* and Barry's father was positioned on the pulpit to be of service. My father was serving as cantor and when he said, "and we bow, and then we kneel before The King of Kings, The Holy One Blessed Be He," my father Harry prostrated himself in a fluid motion with his face approaching the floor. As tradition dictates, he would have risen without moving his feet, typically assisted by a member of the congregation, which in this case was Barry's dad. Barry said it was then that his dad became aware of a particular radiance emanating from our father's *punim (Yiddish for face)*. He likened it to what the special radiance must have been like when Moses descended the Mount. His father told his son, "I believe today I saw the face of G-d in the visage of man."

REK: Barry's beautiful words about your father stayed with you, but all the more so because he painted a picture, an image, a story.

ARK: I have always been captivated by stories. As a caregiver, a willingness to spend the time and listen to a patient's stories is a precious thing for both patient and caregiver. A caregiver must be open to hearing, and a patient has to trust someone outside of themselves. It's an interesting phenomenon that at that moment, someone will begin telling you about themselves. It's natural. They're trying to establish rapport—and by trusting this individual outside their inner circle, they're letting you into their world.

Making time for someone's story and thereby history allows you to better participate in their present and potentially their future.

REK: Did you also share something about yourself?

ARK: You make yourself vulnerable by sharing your own story. It becomes a critical two-way street that requires giving on both sides.

In dealing with patients, I've let them know that I've also been apprehensive about the challenges I face, or frustrated by fear or that recovery is taking so long. By sharing our stories, we're engaging in an embrace of sorts. There's warmth, and there can be humor—and both parties can step away from this dance richer for it.

I hope to bring some measure of equanimity into others' lives. My own studies reinforce my belief in the power of stories, the universality of struggle and the joy of shared experience. ✍

"There is no greater agony than bearing an untold story inside you."

—Maya Angelou, poet, memoirist
and civil rights activist

Above All,
Do No Harm

REK: I powerfully recall when you and Mom traveled to London to meet the nurse who started the modern hospice movement. Did that meeting represent a transition point for you?

ARK: Meeting Dame Cicely Saunders was inspiring and, in a way, helped solidify my own views and belief in the idea of a "good" death and the importance of not losing sight of our professional responsibility to the dictum *Primum non nocere (Latin for "above all, do no harm")*. We don't cure all the illnesses we treat, and sometimes we must accept that our interventions may be therapeutic, but not curative.

I was open-minded and wanted to learn from Dame Cicely and had the privilege of making rounds with her. She in turn asked me lots of questions about American hospice practice. She was professionally interested in how we managed pain control. Morphine was what was used in England, but she had seen the explosion of alternative drug treatments and wanted to make sure that the care of hospice patients wasn't commercialized making money off the backs of the most vulnerable. Her approach was "keep it simple" and focused on what's best for the patients.

I think that as a clinical physician I was in tune with "Above all, do no harm." I had my own strong feelings about the importance of each patient's quality of life, including the *end* of their life. Like every other practicing physician, I witnessed some situations in which the care focus seemed to be on *extending* life rather than preserving life's quality. These decisions are difficult for every practitioner.

When I chaired the medical Ethics Committee at Highland Park Hospital, a case came before us where a family requested that everything possible be done for a mother, who happened to be a Holocaust survivor. In this situation, the patient required pressor therapy (raises blood pressure), which caused pain—and this is when the nurses in the ICU brought the case before the Ethics Committee. They were concerned for the patient's comfort because they felt the family was not focused on the patient's overall well-being but rather measuring the extension of life, seemingly at any cost, as the highest priority.

REK: In this case, how did the Ethics Committee rule, and did the family abide by that recommendation?

ARK: Given the family's religious background, I intuited that they needed to know that their choices were in keeping with Jewish law. I invited the head of the *Beth Din (Hebrew for a Jewish Rabbinical Court of Law)* to hear the case and participate in the conversation of the issues under review. I wanted the *rabbi* to provide an opinion as to whether we were doing what was in the patient's best interest from a Jewish point of view.

He considered that the principle of maintaining life included maintaining the *quality* of life and not just the matter of time. This becomes the inverse of the principle of "do no harm" because to maintain her life was causing physical distress. She was suffering, and that's what the *rabbi* focused on. In his assessment, delaying her death was extending her suffering, and this was counter to his interpretation of the Jewish law. The family, armed with this knowledge, deferred to the advice of the ICU care team and therapeutic adjustments were made.

REK: Communicating information with patients and families has to be a daunting task at times.

ARK: Life is in constant fluctuation—and as caregivers, we are seeking to maintain a kind of balance knowing there are consequences to every intervention. Ultimately, we're working to alleviate suffering—which often is more than purely a physical circumstance.

It's always imperative that an individual receiving care and their family recognize the risks associated with potential therapies or medications. There's an added dimension and weight to such conversations with families around end-of-life care, particularly in situations where the patient has not clearly spelled out their wishes with an advance directive, or at least talked about what they want in an end-of-life situation. But the physician/caregiver has to be willing to accept the challenge of beginning or maintaining the dialogue.

There has to be a willingness to have an open exchange of information where real information is shared, not hidden. I've had patients ask me, "Am I going to live through this?" Like many physicians, I have also had patients' family members raise those kinds of questions. It has been most challenging when family members, overcome with anxiety and anticipating grief, threaten the care team to do whatever it takes to save the patient. They may perceive that the patient is ready to let go and may be unprepared and consequently unwilling for a final goodbye.

I've tried to help patients, and their families, face the reality of their clinical situation and to be prepared for all outcomes, including death. Most of all, though, I've had to keep my eye on what the patient wants and practice "do no harm," which often can mean clarifying a patient's wishes to their family.

I think the American medical community has made progress toward this end, yet it is still difficult for many to give voice to the idea of death and dying. They may see it as their own failure.

REK: How did you get to the place that you were so comfortable having those conversations with patients?

ARK: A team approach may work best now, and the ultimate goal is for that patient to experience love. But for me, I had to get over my fear of failing. We can't as caregivers always transition someone from a state of disease to a state of health, so we have to think about what our options are. I think as caregivers we have to be willing to be present and to be in attendance to someone as they're dying.

I remember making home visits to individuals who were dying, and it was a heartening feeling to see someone at home surrounded by family members who cared and who were doing everything in their power to make their loved one comfortable.

Conversely, I remember very well a patient at Highland Park Hospital whom I knew from synagogue who had a very hard death, as she had such trouble letting go. She possessed a steel exterior and seemed unable to relax. To the staff's amazement, once her dog cuddled next to her, she settled, her breathing became less labored and her eyes closed.

With every patient I encountered in the final stages of life, I learned something new, and I felt a deep pull at a personal level. I know now, and knew then, what I want and need around my own death. As much as anybody can hope and pray for their final wishes to be fulfilled, I fervently hope to be surrounded by loved ones; to receive patience and comfort from family, friends and caregivers; and to know that as my own needs continue to evolve, they will be heard and respected by those dear to me.

I have tried to figure out how to help others explore what they want and need. Maybe selfishly I wanted to pay particular attention so I could make my own life more meaningful and make sure I integrate in my mind that my eventual death is a true part of the full circle of life.

REK: And how *do you* want your death to go?

ARK: I want to be surrounded by people who are attentive to those last minutes of life. Someone respectful in the face of a deteriorating body…ready to hear my *viduy (Hebrew for confession).*

REK: Throughout your life, I know you've worked with hospice and palliative care as a way to try to help others, outside of a clinical setting, become more comfortable with the ultimate reality of death.

ARK: At the most basic level, I've encouraged family, friends and colleagues to write an ethical will. *(See the Afterword on page 155.)*

At a broader, more theological level, I believe in a hereafter. I accept the fact that my soul will move on as something real, and because of that, I'm not as fearful about the physical changes and demise of my body. This is a metaphysical pass-through state; I accept that there are other worlds for us out there.

I believe there is a way to behave when someone is exiting the world, and I believe there's an honorable way for us to exit this world. I believe there's a place for helping someone who is suffering—the ultimate relief of suffering, when you have patients directly asking to be free of their pain and anguish in the end stages of an incurable disease— that actually fulfills your responsibility as a healer.

REK: You're saying...

ARK: I believe in a spectrum from sedation to physician-assisted suicide for terminally ill patients.

REK: How is that orientation perceived by fellow caregivers and doctors in particular?

ARK: I think the perspective is changing, and more physicians are making peace with the idea that it should be the patient's choice, if they are of sound mind to make that decision. I hoped my own work on the Ethics Committee and the Center for Compassion in Medical Care has helped, in its own small way, to open up uncomfortable dialogues among physicians, and particularly physicians of different generations.

Trust and respect are so important. We as individuals have to realize we may not have all the answers, but we can ask questions—and someone will feel heard and collectively we can come up with the best solutions. ✐

....

"I've learned that people will forget what you said, people will forget what you did, but people will never forget how you made them feel."

—*Maya Angelou, poet, memoirist and civil rights activist*

....

We All Have
a Spark

REK: As we bring our conversation to a close, for now, do you have any other messages for your reader?

ARK: To be present. And to nurture the spark in each of us that helps us make the difference that only each of us as individuals can make.

REK: To be present?

ARK: Once while walking in the Jewish Quarter in Israel, Kerana and I passed an artist with artistic renderings of biblical quotes. The one that caught my eye, which now hangs in our home, was a representation of G-d's command to "be present." In that moment, it was as if the words jumped out and grabbed my collar and said, "Hey, listen fella—what's going on here and what does G-d want from you?" That was how powerful the artist's brush was in letting me really hear the message.

A loose translation of the quote from Micah 6:8 begins *"Hegid Lecham Adam"* and in English is "What the Holy One Blessed Be He wants from you in this world is not just to be just, but also to love kindness and to walk humbly with G-d as you search for the awe and for the beauty in each day."

REK: So, humility is part of being present?

ARK: That is how I find my way to being centered and present. While the experience in Israel was powerful and very grounding, that is not an everyday occurrence. In the *Chassidic* world, the great-grandson of the *Baal Shem Tov*, Rebbe Nachman of Breslov, said it in the following way: "What is our individual obligation but to know that there is a spark of goodness in everyone. And our obligation is to be alert to its presence, help to nourish it and firmly imprint its validity/value as a condition of life."

These themes are also articulated with even more focus in the 34th Psalm of David. My interpretive understanding of that Psalm is: "What is the purpose in living, who is able to love each day, to see the goodness in it?" It goes on to say there will be challenges and you will have to distance yourself from what is bad and struggle for the good. We're living in the presence of a world that tests our mettle on a daily basis. The Psalm concludes: "Request, implore the best from the next person. Drawing out with peaceful intent, focus on finding a way for balance. Add to the peace of the universe. And pursue it."

REK: And the spark?

ARK: You start with the spark, identify its presence, recognize it, and raise the flame so it illuminates and produces energy. Whatever that might be.

What encourages me each day is the same spirit with which G-d created the world. With all its glory. Humans have free will. It is very powerful to me that we have the choice. The more we understand the dynamics and responsibility of freedom, the more we can channel energy for the ultimate good of the universe.

From a Jewish perspective, free will is associated with the Big Bang. The explosive energy that attended the release of the Big Bang contained divine energy. I love the thought that there is divinity in the human condition and by directing our freedom of choice to goodness, we share our spark with the world. 🕮

"Someone I loved once gave me a box of darkness.
It took me years to realize that this, too, was a gift."

—*Mary Oliver, Pulitzer Prize-winning
American poet*

Afterword

Thank you for traveling with me.

My enormous gratitude to a world of people who may be unnamed on these pages but who have touched me in so many ways. Their kindness is exhilarating and cannot be unspoken. They kindle in me a deep desire to give more of myself. Opening up to the goodness in the world and experiencing the many gifts of the universe is a blessing in my life.

Before we part ways for now, I want to make an invitation.

I invite you to consider what is most important to you in this world. What do you care enough about that you would place that above all other things? These are most likely your core values. They're probably fundamental beliefs. They're guiding principles for your daily living.

With this in hand, begin crafting what I would call your Ethical Will. Take pen and paper or sit in front of your laptop. Just start writing. This is a way to share not only your values, life's lessons, hopes and dreams for the future, but also your blessings and expressions of love and forgiveness for those you hold most dear. It is not a document for the end of days but rather for your every day. An Ethical Will is something anyone can create, live by and share. It can also be modified since it should be a living document. This will be a gift both to yourself and to anyone who makes up your immediate community.

> *"Please remember that I love each of you for who you are. I accept you fully with your strengths and limitations and with all of your complexities. I do this for myself as well.*

> *"Lead your life fully, find your happiness, and love and respect those with whom you share your days and years.*

> *"Please know that though I have tried to live by example and tried to be a good example, I am a human with frailties and if I have hurt, injured or diminished you because of my limitations, I ask you to forgive me.*

> *"B'ahava b'lee sof, with unending love."*

> —An excerpt from Avram R. Kraft's Ethical Will

I'm reminded of the dictum of our father *"ain davor ha'omade lifne haratzon"* loosely translated as *"the power of your will is unbounded."* If you will it, it can happen.

We do the footwork and let the Divine Being know our intentions. The world today is far from ideal. There are so many pushes and pulls that challenge our equilibrium. At moments like these, it's easy to make it about ourselves. What do *I* need? How do *I* maintain my composure? That moment can also be an inward reminder to look outside ourselves. *V'ahavta l'reacha kamocha (Hebrew for "And you shall love your friend as you love yourself,"* Leviticus 19:18).

The universal golden rule we learn as a child can serve us for a lifetime.

Go forward, undaunted and with a full and open heart.

I close with two sincere wishes:

I wish that each of us might search out the well-spring of love to heal and to bond wherever we are in our world and on our journey.

And I wish that we might be ready in the moment to experience the majesty of the unknown.

Thank you,

Avram

January 2019 / 5779 (Jewish lunar calendar)

Acknowledgments

The obligation of being a compassionate caregiver has emerged from the daily application of being an assistant to the "True Healer" (found in the Book of Exodus). Nothing is done alone. Everything is accomplished with interdependence.

It's been a team effort for every stage of my developmental growth as a person dedicated to the art of the healing sciences.

I recognize that my learning and understanding emerge from every patient who was my teacher and every teacher who was my mentor, from every classroom to every clinical setting. This cross-pollination has fueled me at my very core, and as an individual I learn because of this remarkable exposure to the human condition with all its vulnerability, opportunity and frailty.

I begin with thanks for those who brought me into this world and stewarded my development as a young man, Sarah and Harry Kraft. I learned about interdependence as a child with my beloved siblings Robert and Elizabeth (Levine). To this day, they offer me singular support and love.

To my wife, you know what's in my heart and head and the dedication of this book is to you. To our children Adam and Rachel, you were my earliest audience members while I prepared for academic presentations. Your childlike wonder and queries kept me on the straight and narrow in my own quest for a grounded reality, and your kind and compassionate souls are so fully developed in your adulthood. I love you both dearly.

To my mentors in medical school Dr. Arthur Gladstone (my father-in-law) and Dr. William Stahl. Their clinical commitment was the stimulus to my becoming a surgeon. Arthur Gladstone not only taught me the art of surgery, assisting me during the first operation I performed, but also secured a summer position in that hospital for his daughter, a nursing student at UVM, for which I am forever grateful as that is where Kerana and I began our romance.

There were surgical masters who trained residents to become mature practitioners. Many stand out, including Robert Zollinger and William Silen who set standards for generations of surgeons.

From the operating room at Cook County Hospital to its Ethics Committee.

From Departments of Surgery at the University of Vermont to the University of Illinois to the Department of Medicine at Northwestern University.

To my dear colleagues at Highland Park Hospital, where I have particular fondness for the decades I practiced surgery in an intimate and supportive environment I called my medical home.

The outgrowth of a lifetime of this work led to the creation of the Center for Compassion in Medical Care (CCMC) at Evanston Northwestern Healthcare (ENH), now NorthShore University HealthSystem (NorthShore). The Center was established through the generous support of The Robert and Myra Kraft Family Foundation making a longtime personal dream a reality.

Schwartz Rounds was one of the key programs for the CCMC. It was the essential true north, an internal guiding compass. It was founded by Ken Schwartz at the Massachusetts General Hospital in the days before his death to nurture compassion in health care. My time in Boston with Marjorie Stanzler and others enabled me to initiate our own Schwartz Rounds under the auspices of ENH. Schwartz Rounds provided a standard for bringing together every layer of the hospital, from doctors and nurses to custodial staff, for an open discussion around the care of our patients.

A loving acknowledgment of my late son-in-law Michael Maggio who was a remarkable participant in early conversations about the CCMC.

In doing this work, I would be remiss in not recognizing the essential roles of Dr. Janardan (Janu) D. Khandekar, Chairman of the Department of Medicine at NorthShore; Mark R. Neaman, former President and CEO of NorthShore; Dr. Michael Graham of Evanston Hospital; my co-facilitator Dr. John Roland of the Chicago Center for Family Health; Pastor John Grindler Katonah, former Chaplain Coordinator at NorthShore and Schwartz Rounds Consultant; Dr. Philippe Cochran, current Ethics Committee Chair at

NorthShore; and Debbie Szczesniak, former Executive Assistant, CCMC.

For 40 years, Kerana and I have belonged to a Sabbath Study group that has been a bimonthly gathering of friendship and biblical study. These families formed a nucleus of guidance and wisdom during my professional years and beyond and were a critical source of support during the formation of the CCMC: Fran and Bernie Alpert, Hetty and Al DeLeeuwe, Mona and Buzzy Fishbane, Penina and Reuven Frankel, Barbara and David Hoffman, Bonnie and Abba Lessing, Betsy and Michael Katz, Fran and Joel Rabinowitz, Tziona and David Silverman, and Isabel and Al Soffer.

Throughout my life, many trusted souls challenged my thinking, which was an essential part of my growth. Sometimes they were peers like my private practice partners Edward Margulies, Earl Norman and Steve Haggerty. At other times it was friends like Henry Hollander and Steve Kaufman who introduced me to new ways of thinking and new technology.

It was my religious teachers who guided me through study of ancient text, which led me to a contemporary understanding of the world around me and myself. These included Moshe Lieberman and Egon Lewin from my childhood as well as adult guides like Rabbi David Englander, Dr. Michael (Buzzy) Fishbane, Rabbi William Hamilton, Rabbi Vernon Kurtz, Rabbi William H. Lebeau, Rabbi Michael Schwab, Rabbi Yossi Shanowitz, Rabbi David Steinhardt, Rabbi Michel Twerski, Rabbi Asher Weil and my current mentor Rabbi Joseph P. Schultz, PhD.

In my adult study, I've been blessed with a study partner in David Hoffman who has touched me deeply with his own questioning and compassion.

I have spoken openly about periods of darkness and emotional turbulence. Kerana and I are grateful for the generous spirit and stellar expertise of Dr. Rudolf Kaelbling and Dr. Raymond M. Silverman.

A limitless thank you goes to Fran and Bernie Alpert and Barbara and David Hoffman for always being there for us. So grateful!

Kerana and I are also grateful for the friendship and spiritual wisdom of Claudia Kaplan Mandelbaum.

To Joyce Sobczyk, all we can say is thank you for the many ways you support us both.

And to my son-in-law Doug Brown, I am grateful for your openness, your extraordinary ability to listen and for all the perceptive insights you share. And thank you for your willingness to support the many, many hours that Rachel and I devoted to this book.

And to my collaborators on the book, my deepest appreciation:

To the individuals who made themselves available to Susan White for interviews for the project: Bernie and Fran Alpert, Dr. Philippe L. Cochran, Kerana Gladstone Kraft, Rabbi William Hamilton, Barbara and David Hoffman, Henry Hollander, Dr. Alan Katz, Betsy and Michael Katz, and Rabbi Joe Schultz.

To those whose life stories were an inspiration including my parents, Egon Lewin, Moshe Lieberman, Art Moore and an 8-year-old named Nick.

To our gentle readers Jennifer Gladstone and Kim Swift, I thank you for your thoughtful comments and insightful edits.

To our proofreaders Rabbi Daniel Bronstein for the Hebrew and biblical text and Becky Keen for the manuscript as a whole, my appreciation.

To our designer Sarah Stec, your artistry has been invaluable.

This text was developed over the past three years with two primary partners, Susan White and my daughter Rachel. Susan and Rachel helped me cull through years of my own journal entries and articles to fashion the questions that led to these interviews. They have been invaluable editors and trusted confidantes.

Susan, you have been an extended family member since you were Rachel's college roommate, and then we developed our own partnership when we worked together at Evanston Northwestern Healthcare. I am grateful for your firm guidance and caring soul.

And to Rachel, I cannot adequately find the words to express my appreciation for your commitment to this labor of love. I have expressed to you privately my gratitude for your invaluable contribution that competed with time for yourself, your husband and other priorities. You have harmonized with me and let me close by saying that the culmination of this project is because of your gentle tenacity, wisdom and love.

*I remember well the inscription my father Harry
wrote in 1971 to my mother Sarah in a
daily prayer book, five years before his death:*

"We praise the Lord for His goodness.
 May He continue to shower His blessings upon you,
 my beloved, as each day begins."

Glossary

Ahavat shalom bain adam I'rayahu Hebrew for making peace among people.

Ain davor ha'omade lifne haratzon Hebrew phrase loosely translated as "the power of your will is unbounded."

Al tomar, do not say

Aliyah Hebrew meaning ascent—in addition to referring to the move from outside of Israel to live in Israel, it also refers to chanting the blessings before and after reading the **Torah**.

"Am I my brother's keeper" Genesis 4:9.

Baal Shem Tov, founder of **Chassidism**. Its followers strive to develop a joyous relationship with G-d and are guided in this goal by the teachings of **Rabbi (or Rebbe) Nachman of Breslov,** the Baal Shem Tov's great-grandson.

B'ahava b'lee sof Hebrew for "with unending love."

Bar Mitzvah Hebrew for a Jewish Coming of Age ritual for a boy of 13. It is Bat Mitzvah for a girl at the age of 12. See also **Mitzvah**

Beth Din Hebrew for a Jewish Rabbinical Court of Law.

Bimah Hebrew for pulpit.

Breaking of the vessels See **Shevirat ha-kelim**.

Brit milah Hebrew for the covenant of circumcision, between a Jewish male on the eighth day of life and the Divine Being. Pronounced "bris" in Yiddish.

B'shert Yiddish for destiny as in destined to happen and often referring to a soulmate.

Chassidic relating to Chassidism, its members, their belief or practices. Chassidism is an ultra-orthodox branch of Judaism that draws heavily on the Jewish mystical tradition of prayer and ritual to pursue a direct experience of G-d.

Chumash Hebrew for the five books of the **Torah**.

Days of Awe See **High Holidays**.

Dor l' dor Literally means generation to generation in Hebrew with a broader meaning of the passing down of tradition from generation to generation.

Ein d'var ha-omed bifnay haratzon... Hebrew for "There is nothing that if you will it, that can't be accomplished." —credited to a variety of sources including the **Zohar** (Vol. 2. P. 162b), the Lubavitcher Rebbe Yosef Yitzchak Schneerson and Zionist leader Menachem Ussishkin.

Elohim/Elokim Elohim is the general way of referring to G-d in modern Hebrew. The "k" in "Elokim" is how it is pronounced by religious Jews who wish to avoid using G-d's name.

Erev Shabbat Hebrew for the eve of the Sabbath.

Gemilut chasadim Hebrew for acts of loving kindness.

Hegid Lecham Adam Hebrew and is the beginning of Micah 6:8 that translates in English as "What the Holy One Blessed Be He wants from you in this world is not just to be just, but also to love kindness and to walk humbly with G-d as you search for the awe and for the beauty in each day."

High Holidays In Hebrew, it is called **Yamim Noraim**, also known as the **Days of Awe**—the time between **Rosh Hashanah** and **Yom Kippur** to the celebration of **Sukkot** honoring the period in Jewish history when the Jews moved from Egypt to the Holy Land.

Ki ani Hashem rofecha Hebrew for "For I am the Lord that heals you" (Exodus 15:26).

Kohe v'etzem yadee ahsa lee at hahayil hazeh Hebrew for "[only through] the strength of my hand I did this powerful thing" (Isaiah 10:13).

Kotel Hebrew for the ancient retaining limestone wall in the Old City of Jerusalem also known as the Western Wall.

May the memory of the righteous be for a blessing See **Of blessed memory**.

Menachem avel Hebrew for consoling mourners.

Menachem avel zein The last word ("zein") is Yiddish, and the expression means to visit and comfort mourners.

Minyan Hebrew for "to be counted" and refers to a gathering of at least 10 people for a prayer service—in a more traditional setting, it would be 10 men.

Mitzvah Hebrew for commandment, with a secondary meaning of good deed.

Modeh ani lifanekha melekh chai v'kayam shehechezarta bi nishmahti Hebrew for "I give thanks before you, living and eternal King, for You have returned within me my soul with compassion; abundant is Your faithfulness!"—a prayer recited in the morning, traditionally before getting out of bed.

M'sader kiddushin Hebrew for marriage officiant.

M'zmor L'todah Hebrew for A Psalm of Thanksgiving.

Naaseh v'nshmah Hebrew for "act and hear." The whole quote is "act and hear, do the **mitzvah**—the good deed—and then reflect, learn and teach" (Exodus 24:3).

Nigun Hebrew for melody and typically without words.

Of blessed memory A Jewish expression to honor the deceased.

Ohave shalom, v'rodef shalom, ohave et habriot umkurvan latorah Hebrew for "he loved peace, he pursued peace, he loved G-d's creatures and brought them closer to the **Torah**" (*Pirkei Avot,* 1:12, *Ethics of the Fathers*).

Olam HaBah Hebrew for the afterlife.

Pesach Hebrew for Passover, the Jewish holiday commemorating G-d's redemption of the Jews from slavery in Egypt.

Pirkei Avot Hebrew for *Chapters of the Fathers*, also called *Sayings of the Fathers* and *Ethics of the Fathers*. Part of Talmudic literature.

Primum non nocere Latin for "above all, do no harm."

Punim Yiddish for face.

Rabbi Originates from the Hebrew word for teacher, trained and ordained for Jewish leadership.

Rabbi (or Rebbe) Nachman of Breslov One of the most creative and influential **Chassidic rabbis** and founder of the Breslov **Chassidic** sect, and a great-grandson of the **Baal Shem Tov**, founder of Chassidism. Its followers strive to develop a joyous relationship with G-d and are guided in this goal by the teachings of Rebbe Nachman.

Rabbinate Hebrew for the collective institution of **rabbis**.

Rebbe Yiddish for **rabbi**.

Rosh Hashanah Hebrew for the Head of the Year, the Jewish New Year.

Seder Hebrew for Order and refers to the **Passover** meal during which the story of the Hebrew exodus from Egypt is retold.

Semicha Hebrew for becoming a rabbi.

Shabbat Hebrew for Sabbath.

Shabbos Yiddish for Sabbath.

Shalom Aleichem Hebrew for "Peace be unto you" and the blessing from the biblical book of Bemidbar (Hebrew for Numbers) 6:24-27 engenders love and peace. This is sung in Hebrew as the Sabbath is ushered in.

Shevirat ha-kelim Hebrew for the **breaking of the vessels**, a concept derived from Jewish mystical tradition teaching that at creation, the vessels containing G-d's essence were broken. In turn, we are supposed to reconstitute the vessels, gather G-d's essence by perfecting the world as it now stands via **Tikkun Olam** (Hebrew for repairing the world).

Shlaimut Hebrew for wholeness.

Shofar Hebrew for a ram's horn trumpet sounded during **Rosh Hashanah** and **Yom Kippur**, a Jewish holiday obligation of the **Torah** for those who may not be able to hear the shofar blown in synagogue during the **High Holidays**.

Shul Yiddish for synagogue.

Siddarim Hebrew plural for **Passover meal** (singular is **seder**).

Siddur Hebrew for prayer book.

Siddurim Hebrew plural for **prayer books** (singular is **siddur**).

Sukkot The Holy Days of the Feast of Tabernacles.

Tallis Hebrew for prayer shawl.

Talmud An ancient collection of writings including exposition of Jewish law intermingled with parables. Alongside the **Torah**, the Talmud is the foundational text of Judaism about both Jewish law and Jewish tradition.

Tikkun Olam Hebrew for the Jewish concept meaning to repair the world with acts of kindness. It has been interpreted by some on the mystical level (see **Shevirat ha-kelim** Hebrew for breaking the vessels) while others view it as actualized through social justice.

Torah In Hebrew, the "teaching" or "way" of Judaism. Depending on the context, Torah can refer to the first third of the Bible, also known as the five books of Moses or **Chumash**; Torah can also refer to the entirety of the Bible, or the entirety of traditional Jewish texts including the **Talmud**. Finally, contemporaneous insights can also be referred to as "Torah."

V'ahavta et Hashem Elochecha bekhol - levavavkha u'vekhol nafshekha u'vekhol me'odekha Hebrew for "And you shall love the Lord, your God, with all of your heart, soul and might…" from the prayer "The Shema," Deuteronomy 6:4-5.

V'ahavta l'reacha kamocha Hebrew for "And you shall love your friend as you love yourself" (Leviticus 19:18).

V'hafachta Bo… Hebrew for the beginning of a maxim of Rabbi Ben Bag Bag who says, "Search in it and search in it, since everything is in it. And in it should you look, and grow old and be worn in it, and from it do not move, since there is no characteristic greater than it" (from *Pirkei Avot, Sayings of the Fathers*, 5:22).

Yamim Noraim Hebrew for **Rosh Hashanah** and **Yom Kippur**.

Yom Kippur Hebrew for the Day of Atonement.

Y'simeach Hebrew for "May G-d make you like."

Y'simeach Elohim k'Sarah, k'Rivkah, k'Rachel, uk'Leah
Hebrew for "May G-d make you like Sarah, Rebecca,
Rachel and Leah" (Numbers 6:24-26). Priestly blessing
recited by parents on Friday night, at the start of the
Sabbath, to their daughters. (For sons, it's **Y'simeach
Elohim k'Ephraim v'Menashe** Hebrew for "May G-d make
you like Ephraim and Menashe."

Viduy Hebrew for confession.

Zohar The foundational text of the Jewish mystical
tradition and the preeminent text of Kabbalah (Hebrew for
"reception"; a text containing ancient and medieval Jewish
exposition of a mystical interpretation of the **Torah**).

Collaborators

Rachel E. Kraft is Avram's daughter and has enjoyed a 30-year arts administration career with a particular focus on nonprofit theater.

Susan J. White is a former journalist, a longtime professional writer and a close friend of the Kraft family.

Sarah Stec: Book Design

Made in the USA
Monee, IL
08 December 2019